The Butterflies of Northern Europe

Björn Dal

Edited by Michael Morris
Translated by Roger Littleboy

CROOM HELM
London & Canberra

© 1978 Björn Dal. © 1982 English edition and translation Croom Helm
Croom Helm Ltd, 2–10 St John's Road, London SW11

British Library Cataloguing in Publication Data

Dal, Björn   ·
    The butterflies of northern Europe.
    1. Butterflies—Europe, Northern—Identification
    I. Title   II. Morris, Michael
    595.78'9'094   QL555.A1

ISBN 0–7099–0810–5

Printed and bound in Portugal

Contents

Introduction

This volume is an introduction to the butterflies of northern Europe in general and the British Isles in particular. All the species which are found regularly in Britain and the northern European countries have been included, with the exception of the truly 'high Arctic' butterflies of the extreme north, which are not often found below the Arctic Circle. Species of casual or unusual occurrence in northern Europe have also been omitted; the beginner would be unlikely, as well as fortunate, to come across any species not mentioned in this book. The guide is intended to be both a northern summary of, and a supplement to, the standard work on European butterflies, *A Field Guide to the Butterflies of Britain and Europe*, Lionel Higgins and Norman Riley, 3rd edn (Collins, London, 1975). This classic work of reference is deservedly popular and has been translated into most European languages, and its illustrations, by Brian Hargreaves, are excellent and accurate, although only 'set' or museum specimens are depicted. However, many beginners may find that the book's sheer comprehensiveness can be discouraging. A simpler guide to the more limited fauna of northern Europe, emphasising field characteristics of ecology and behaviour, would seem to be more useful to the non-professional.

In most books on butterflies, including Higgins and Riley, the species are arranged systematically, that is, in the order in which they are classified, with whites together in one place, fritillaries in another, and so on. This is most appropriate for a museum but is less natural for a field guide, particularly one restricted to a fairly small fauna. This why we have arranged the species according to the kind of terrain or biotope (often called habitat) in which they are found. The arrangement by biotopes is not only helpful to the beginner, who is probably familiar with the main ones and can thus identify an observed butterfly more easily, but is ecologically important. The caterpillars of each butterfly species are dependent upon various host plants or foodplants; some species are restricted to a very few different kinds of plant, or even to only one. Because some foodplants grow only in particular places, butterflies are often limited to one or two biotopes. Some, however, are able to feed on several foodplants, or are strong-flying or wide-ranging, and are thus not restricted to one biotope. In this volume these species are included under two or more biotopes, but one has usually been chosen as the principal one in which the species occurs, and there is one main illustration of each butterfly species. Unlike a systematic classification, arrangement by biotopes cannot be exact, so there is some overlap of species' requirements; also, the habitats of some British species are slightly different from those of northern Europe.

The chief aid to identification of species in this guide is the illustrations; no key of the traditional type is provided. Indentification of any animal or plant is easier when the choice of alternatives is limited. We have restricted the fauna of European butterflies by considering only a relatively small geographical area (Britain and northern Europe), and further reduced them by reference to different biotopes. Remember, however, that mobile insects like butterflies may occasionally be found in the 'wrong' biotope and in a very few cases the whole volume may have to be searched to identify one butterfly in an unusual biotope.

When we refer to different 'kinds' of butterfly we usually mean species. However, many butterfly species exist in several different and recognised races or subspecies. 'Major' subspecies were described in Higgins and Riley and those that occur in Britain or nothern Europe are included in this volume. Some other subspecies, not mentioned by Higgins and Riley, have also been referred to,

Camberwell Beauties, after hibernating, fly near a birch tree in sap.

5

described or illustrated here. However, the status of subspecies is less easy to determine than the validity of species and it is probable that not all the subspecies recognised here will be found to be of equal standing. More breeding and other biological work is needed, in many cases, to establish the exact status of some 'subspecies'.

The species and subspecies of each butterfly described in the guide are listed on pp. 124–5. The genus, species or subspecies is followed by the name of its author in Roman type (or the initials L. or F. for Linnaeus and Fabricius, two well-known biologists of the late eighteenth century who described many butterflies). This index is a checklist of all the species of butterfly occurring in northern Europe, but the checklist of subspecies from the area is not complete, for the reasons outlined above.

Each illustration is of an actual specimen, rather than an average or idealised example of the species. Nearly all previous books on butterflies, whether intended for use in the field or not, show set specimens whose fore-wings are positioned so that the hind-margin is at right-angles to the body. The setting of butterflies with their wings in this unnatural position has been in general use for about two hundred years. It is favoured by museum workers because almost the entire wing surface is then exposed, which permits observation and measurement of the wings and their markings for the description, comparison and determination of each species. It is unusual, however, for living butterflies to hold their wings in this 'museum' position. The visual impression of a butterfly in its natural surroundings is a pattern formed by the position of the wings relative to each other. Consequently the impressions given by living and museum specimens are different, even allowing for the lack of movement in the latter. The traditional pictures of set butterflies are useful in the identification of specimens in a cabinet drawer or storebox. Illustrating the wings in a natural position is, however, essential for anyone who watches butterflies in their natural environment. Therefore, in most cases we show the wings on one side of the insect in the direct view of the observer, with the wings of the other side pointing at him with their pattern invisible. Those species which are so difficult to distinguish that they must be set for the purpose are usually illustrated by enlarged figures of individual wings so that direct comparison can be made with those of similar species.

External characteristics of butterflies

The Latin name for butterflies and moths is *Lepidoptera*, which means scale-wings. In addition to their scale-covered wings, butterflies and most moths are distinguished from other insects, among other characteristics, by their suctorial tongue or proboscis in the form of a tube, which is kept rolled under the head like a clock spring when not in use.

The body is in three parts: head, thorax and abdomen. As in all insects and other arthropods, the skeleton is an external one. The body is encased in a more or less rigid integument (hard outer skin) which not only protects the insect but also imposes structural limitations on movement and, particularly, growth. The bodies of butterflies and moths, like their wings, are covered with scales. These body scales usually contain a proportion of long narrow ones which look like hairs.

The head is articulated to the thorax and bears compound eyes, mouth-parts and antennae. Most of its surface consists of the compound eyes, which have between 3,000 and 18,000 facets. Below the eyes is a pair of palps, between which lies the proboscis. This is formed from a pair of greatly modified mouth-parts which, in less specialised insects, lie next to the mandibles or jaws and are called maxillae. In butterflies they are elongated and joined together to form a tube through which liquids can be sucked.

The thorax consists of three segments, each with a pair of legs; the front pair is reduced in size in some families. A pair of wings, attached to the two hind-segments of the thorax, consists of thin double membranes stretched on the veins or ribs of the wing. Both surfaces of the wings are covered with overlapping scales arranged like roof tiles. These scales give the wings their pattern and colouring, either because of their pigments or from their structure which refracts the light, producing 'structural' colours. The very long scales at the edges of the wings form the wing fringes. Males often have scent-scales on the wings which exude mating scents or pheromones, important in courtship and copulation. The scent-scales look quite different from normal scales; they may be distributed over the entire surface of the wing, or concentrated in patches or lines. These are usually dark in colour and often the easiest means of distinguishing males from females.

The abdomen is segmented and articulated. The sexual organs, with hard and chitinous external parts, are located at its tip. The male's abdomen is usually more or less cylindrical along its entire length and has an anal tuft of scales. The

How shape and marking can change, depending on the position of the wings. Poplar Admiral (left) with wings set in the position normally used in collections. On the right is the same specimen with its wings in their natural position.

female's is rounded and dilated with the eggs and internal reproductive organs and somewhat pointed at the tip. The sex of a butterfly may be determined from the differences in the tip of the abdomen: the male bears the genital claspers in the anal tuft, while in the female only the extremity of the ovipositor, the organ which actually places the eggs on their foodplants, is obvious. In addition, of course, male and female may vary in their wing colour and markings (secondary sexual characters).

Classification

Because there are so many different insect species, entomologists are particularly concerned with their description, naming and classification. The almost universally adopted system of classification is a 'natural' or 'phylogenetic' one: the classification reflects the affinity of one species with another and summarises its evolution. Classification is thus by no means aimed solely at producing an orderly arrangement of species, and entomologists frequently pay attention to small details of structure and coloration which might be thought trivial but for their importance to our understanding of evolutionary processes.

Classification is a hierarchical arrangement of categories which have special names and reflect more or less uniform levels of organisation, and affinity of their constituent groups throughout the animal kingdom, and to some extent the plant kingdom as well. The 'building block' or unit of classification is the species, which is the only one of the categories to have biological (as opposed to systematic) significance. Comprehensive definition of the species is difficult, but the concept of a distinct kind of animal which does not successfully interbreed with any other kind is the central consideration. It is often convenient to refer to a category in classification without actually defining its hierarchical level. For instance, we may

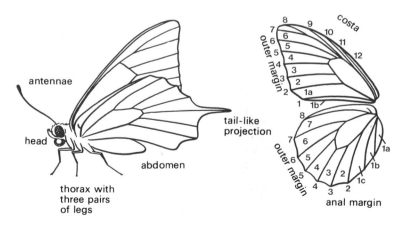

The arrangement of veins (venation) is an important distinguishing feature in classification. Lepidopterists number the veins and the areas between them (cells) so that the position of the wing markings can be clearly described. D = discal cell.

not be sure whether a particular butterfly is a distinct species or a subspecies. In these cases the noncomittal term *taxon* (pl. *taxa*) is very useful in referring to such entities.

Species are grouped together with genera (sing. genus). The name of the genus to which a butterfly belongs is the first element in its scientific name. In the name of the Small White (p. 114), for instance, *Pieris* is the generic name while *rapae* indicates the species and distinguishes it from the closely-related Large and Green-veined Whites, which are also placed in the same genus, *Pieris*. Technically, the specific name of the Small White is *Pieris rapae*, *rapae* being the trivial name or specific epithet; but *rapae* is often, if inaccurately, called the specific name.

Subspecies are distinguished by a third name. For example, *Papilio machaon britannicus* is the name of the British subspecies of the Swallowtail (p. 21), *britannicus* being the subspecific name which distinguishes this particular subspecies from others. In many species, for instance the Meadow Brown (p. 93), the name of one subspecies may be the same as the specific epithet (*Maniola jurtina jurtina*); such subspecies are termed the nominate subspecies. All subspecies, sometimes called biological races, are *taxa* which have become isolated in some way from the rest of the species. Such isolation is almost invariably geographical; indeed, there is still controversy as to whether other kinds of isolation (ecological, behavioural) can result in the formation of subspecies, rather than being a consequence of it.

The term 'form' (f.) is used to describe a variant which occurs continually in a population of butterflies. Such variants are often determined genetically in a simple way. An example is the female form *valesina* of the Silverwashed Fritillary (p. 82). Seasonal variation may be so extreme in some cases that the different generations may be referred to as forms, for example the Map butterfly (p. 46), which has a first generation (f. *levana*) and a second (and sometimes a third) (f. *prorsa*). Variants of a butterfly species which occur only very infrequently are termed 'aberrations' (ab.).

Butterfly genera are grouped into families, whose characteristics are described

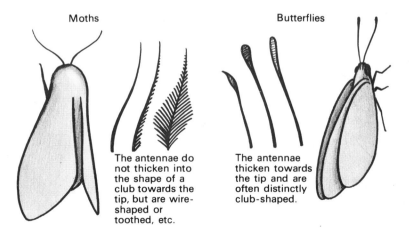

Moths

Butterflies

The antennae do not thicken into the shape of a club towards the tip, but are wire-shaped or toothed, etc.

The antennae thicken towards the tip and are often distinctly club-shaped.

Moth antennae do not have a club but there are many different shapes. The wings, often folded roof-like, point backwards. Butterfly antennae are distinctly club-shaped, although some skippers have a hook. The wings are raised and point upwards.

on pp. 16–17. At one time the butterflies were thought to be a group of equal standing with all other Lepidoptera, and this is reflected in everyday English ('butterflies and moths'). Old textbooks usually distinguish Rhopalocera (butterflies) from Heterocera (moths) and the two terms are sometimes used even today. However, modern classification recognises a grouping of all the families of Lepidoptera into a number of superfamilies. Two of these contain the butterflies: the family Hesperiidae (Skippers) is the only one in the superfamily Hesperioidea, while the remaining butterfly families form the superfamily Papilionoidea. Note that the names of families end in -idae and those of superfamilies in -oidea. This is universal in animal classification. Although there are detailed technical differences between the Hesperioidea and the Papilionoidea on the one hand, and the remainder of the Lepidoptera on the other, all moths have antennae which are not clubbed, or fold their wings like a roof over their bodies, or fly by night. *All* butterflies have clubbed antennae, never fold their wings roof-wise over their bodies, and fly by day (see p. 9).

The butterfly in its environment

You can see butterflies on sunny days from early spring to late autumn, but they are most numerous from May to September. Their life-span (as adult insects) may vary from a fortnight to nearly a year in the case of over-wintering species. Many have just one generation each year. The Peacock (p. 120), for example, emerges in July and flies for several weeks in late summer before hibernating. After re-emergence in the spring, the butterflies mate and the female lays her eggs. The resulting larvae feed up in May and June and when the pupae hatch in July the life cycle is completed. Other single-brooded species over-winter in one of the other three stages—egg, caterpillar or pupa. Several species have two generations a year, and one or two may have three, although rarely more. Several southern European species produce a succession of broods during the summer; this is even more usual in the tropics, although here the incidence of wet and dry seasons may replace the seasons, to some extent, in limiting the number of generations in a year. There can be considerable variation in the pattern of the life cycle, even within the same species. The Small Tortoiseshell (p. 122) is single-brooded in Scandinavia, but has two generations a year in England.

Butterflies, being cold-blooded, can fly only when they have been warmed by the sun. This is why they are never observed in flight very early in the morning. Most species fly only in sunshine but there are several which also fly on warm dull days. Their dependence on sun has made butterflies adapt both physiologically and behaviourally to maximise the heat they obtain from it. You can often watch a butterfly aligning its wings to absorb the sun's heat. On very hot days, however, even butterflies look for shelter, particularly at midday, when they seek the shade of bushes and trees.

Even the beginner will note that there is much variety in types of flight, not only between different species but in the same one, according to circumstances. When the flight is very strong and swift the wings almost touch at the end of both the up stroke and the down stroke. When a butterfly glides, like some of the Nymphalidae in particular, the wings do not move. The maximum speed recorded for a flying butterfly is about 40 k.p.h. for some tropical Skippers, but most flight is much slower.

Adult butterflies are adapted to feed on nectar from flowers. The sugars in nectar provide energy for flight and reproduction. Some species prefer other sweet substances, such as the honeydew excreted by aphids, the sap from trees

Wing movements of a Peacock butterfly in flight.

and the fermenting juices of rotting fruit. A few even feed on urine, moist dung or carrion, presumably because these are sources of nitrogen. In the tropics particularly, but also in Europe, a mass of butterflies will often congregate on a particular patch of moisture.

Flight and feeding can be regarded as ancillary activities to the most important function of the adult butterfly—reproduction. The acts of mating, and later of egg-laying, are often performed in an elaborate and complex manner. Many male (and, to some extent, female) butterflies are strongly territorial. Individuals will defend a short stretch of woodland ride or a patch of sunlight (as in the case of the Speckled Wood, p. 50) against rivals. The encounters of many species, which will fly from the vantage point of a particular leaf or twig apparently to attack passing individuals of the same or different species, result in different behaviour, depending upon whether the intruder is a male or female. An encounter with a receptive, or virgin, female of the same species often leads to complex courtship. Such behaviour obviously varies from species to species. Some, such as the Grayling (p. 73), have elaborate courtship behaviour which has been analysed in detail by animal behaviourists. Mating scents, or pheromones, are very important in courtship and pre-mating behaviour, but visual stimuli also play their part.

The act of copulation may last a few minutes or several hours. The partners are joined tail-to-tail and may often be observed in this position, usually well hidden among the vegetation or inconspicuous on a leaf. Although butterflies are very vulnerable to predators while mating, the coupled pair can fly surprisingly well if disturbed. One of them, usually the larger and stronger female, carries the passive partner in flight.

Butterflies seek out protected spots among vegetation to spend the night or survive during wet and dull weather. Many species take cover at such times, but there are others that roost in the open on grass stems and may be found by assiduous searching. Over-wintering sites, however, need better protection: thick evergreen bushes, hollow trees, fallen branches, houses, stone walls, outhouses and log piles.

The evolution of the characteristic scales of the Lepidoptera has resulted in a wonderful and fascinating diversity of differently patterned and coloured species of butterfly. The functions of these patterns and colours are only partly understood, but it is clear that they are important in the recognition by individuals of others of the same species and in defence against predators.

11

Resting attitudes: (a) wings flat, a characteristic of many Nymphalidae; (b) wings upright, often adopted by Lycaenidae, particularly Hairstreaks; (c) normal wing position of most species; (d) characteristic attitude of many skippers—hind-wings flat and fore-wings at a sharp angle.

Butterflies have many enemies, but insectivorous birds pose a particular threat because they, too, fly by day. The simplest defence against a predator is concealment, and this is the reason for the concealing, or cryptic, patterns and colours of many butterflies. An excellent example is the underside of the Green Hairstreak (p. 58): when it alights on a green leaf after flight and hides its brown upperside by folding its wings, it seems to disappear completely. Many butterflies have eye-spots, or eye-like markings, on the wings, which are used in various ways. In the Peacock (p. 120) the sudden opening of the wings to display the highly coloured 'eyes' will startle a potential predator. In many 'Browns' the eye-spots attract the attention and the beak of an attacking bird, which deflects its assault away from the vulnerable body. Butterflies which have escaped the attack of a bird, but which bear the mark of its beak on the wings, are frequently seen in the field. Butterflies which contain chemicals making them distasteful to predators usually advertise the fact by means of warning colours: the Monarch (p. 18) is a classic example. Palatable species may resemble distasteful ones in both appearance and behaviour. In such cases of 'Batesian mimicry' the palatable butterfly is not eaten by predators because they have learned not to attack the poisonous one (the 'model'). The mimics are usually less numerous than the distasteful models because successful mimicry depends on the predators attacking sufficient models to learn that they are toxic. Other, more complicated, kinds of mimicry are known in butterflies and make the whole subject a remarkable and fascinating one.

Although this field guide concentrates on the adult butterfly, the early stages in the life cycle are equally interesting to observe and study. Because they are usually well-hidden, finding caterpillars, and more particularly eggs and pupae, can be more of a challenge than observing adults. Rearing butterflies from the egg or caterpillar can be very rewarding and collectors could add considerably to our knowledge of these stages.

Each individual butterfly is part of a population. Although the characteristics and behaviour of individuals are fascinating, the study of populations gives more insight into the evolution and ecology of butterflies. Population studies are usually undertaken by professional biologists, but amateur and spare-time entomologists can play their part.

The Camberwell Beauty looks very different against dark and light backgrounds.

Watching butterflies

More and more enthusiasts prefer to watch and study butterflies in the field rather than to form a collection of set specimens. Accurate identification comes with practice and experience, but even the most knowledgeable lepidopterist can make mistakes. Behaviour, habitat and time of appearance are important in determining species, as well as colour and pattern. Differences in lighting and background can dramatically change a butterfly's appearance, as shown in the picture of a Camberwell Beauty (above) against a dark and light background. Most butterflies can be approached quite closely—at least to within one or two metres—but this depends on the species, on temperature and weather generally, and on the skill of the observer. If this is done without noise or sudden movement, many species can be observed from a distance of only a few inches. It is important to be able to do this if serious observation and study is contemplated.

One activity which can be combined with watching butterflies, and used to make a permanent record of observations, is butterfly photography. Details of equipment are beyond the scope of this guide, but keen photographers should note that the development of macrophotography lenses has greatly simplified recording in the field. However, it is expensive compared with just watching.

Conservation

There has been, and is, continuing concern over the widespread decline of butterflies in Britain and Europe. By far the most serious threat to butterflies, as to most other wildlife, is habitat destruction. Land-use changes, particularly the intensification of agriculture and forestry, have been responsible for the local extinction of many colonies of butterflies, while reduction in numbers has been the response of the less sensitive species. Other threats to butterflies are often mentioned, such as the use of pesticides and collecting; neither has been

13

responsible for butterfly destruction on a scale comparable with land-use changes, and it is doubtful whether either has been effective in reducing numbers except in very special circumstances. Nevertheless, collectors should be very sensitive to the need for conservation and should conform to the Code for Insect Collecting produced by, and obtainable from, the Joint Committee for the Conservation of British Insects, $^c/_o$ Royal Entomological Society (address p. 123). In Britain there is a strong conservation movement in which voluntary bodies, such as the County Naturalists' Trusts as well as the official Nature Conservancy Council, take part. Conservationists undertake a multiplicity of necessary tasks and have established a very large number of important nature reserves. Unfortunately, a very few conservationists have adopted a hostile attitude to all forms of collecting, not recognising its importance as an educational, recreative and scientific activity. The butterfly enthusiast who plays his part in reconciling the study of butterflies, through collecting as well as other activities, with conservation is fulfilling a very useful purpose.

M. G. MORRIS

Explanations and abbreviations

The information contained in the descriptions of the species applies to northern Europe; flying periods, choice of biotope, etc. can be different in other parts of the area of distribution of the species.

The scientific names for the plants follow the nomenclature of *Flora Europea.*

Unless otherwise stated, the butterflies have been shown in their natural size.

♂ = male (the sign for the planet Mars)	gen. = generation
♀ = female (the sign for the planet Venus)	spp. = species
ab. = aberration, variant	ssp. = subspecies
f. = form	u = underside

The maps show the present distribution of the species (not the subspecies). Current details are missing in part from eastern Europe, for which reason the shading on the maps for this area may occasionally be inaccurate. The shading for the Fenno-Scandian mountain chain applies also to valleys, etc. which lie below the conifer belt.

Blue and green shows the distribution of the butterfly within the geographical area covered by this book:

Blue indicates those areas outside the actual area of distribution in which the species occurs more or less irregularly.

Green indicates the actual area of distribution of the species. The species is encountered every year within this area in appropriate biotopes.

Yellow shows the approximate distribution of the species in the rest of Europe.

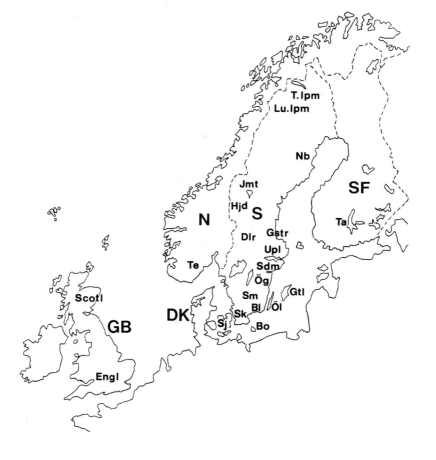

DK = Denmark	Hjd = Härjedalen
Bo = Bornholm	Jmt = Jämtland
Sj = Zealand	Lu. lpm = Lule lappmark
GB = Great Britain	Nb = Norrbotten
Engl = England	Sdm = Södermanland
Scotl = Scotland	Sk = Skåne
N = Norway	Sm = Småland
Te = Telemark	T. lpm = Torne lappmark
S = Sweden	Upl = Uppland
Bl = Blekinge	Ög = Östergötland
Dlr = Dalarna	Öl = Öland
Gstr = Gästrikland	SF = Finland
Gtl = Gotland	Ta = Tavastia

PAPILIONIDAE

Swallowtails and Parnassians
Butterflies of very varied appearance. Only a few species fly in northern Europe. Large or very large butterflies, often elegant gliders. Visitors of flowers.

PIERIDAE

Whites and Yellows
Light, medium-large butterflies of which the species is often difficult to determine. The Cabbage Whites most often have a fluttering flight, whilst the Alpine Clouded Yellow flies fast and low. Visitors to flowers.

NYMPHALIDAE

Fritillaries, Nymphs, etc.
Small to very large butterflies, with very varied appearance. The large species are often highly coloured and are fast fliers. The High Brown Fritillary and various other Fritillaries can most easily have their species determined from the marking on the under-surface of the rear wing. The majority are visitors of flowers.

SATYRIDAE
Browns
Small or medium-large butterflies, most often brown in colour and with eye markings. Some fly fast: Grayling, Rock Grayling and Baltic Grayling; others usually have a slow, fluttering flight. Most are visitors of flowers.

NEMEOBIIDAE
Dukes or Metalmarks
A small family with only one species in Europe: the Duke of Burgundy Fritillary, which rarely visits flowers.

LYCAENIDAE
Blues, Coppers and Hairstreaks
Small butterflies which are usually most easily identified by the markings on the undersides of the wings. The Hairstreaks are, as their name suggests, fast fliers, brown in colour and with a tail-like projection on the rear wing. The Coppers are marked in clear, orange or purple colours. The Blues are blue or brown, the females usually being brown. Most are visitors of flowers.

HESPERIIDAE
Skippers
Small butterflies with a fast, swirling flight. The species are often difficult to distinguish between. Certain skippers are dark with light spots, other skippers are marked in gold, gold-brown or brown. Many are visitors of flowers.

Danaus plexippus *Milkweed or Monarch*

This migratory butterfly is occasionally encountered in western Europe but is not native. In the last century about two hundred examples have been found in the British Isles. The species was originally native to North America, but reached New Zealand in 1840, Australia in 1870 and the Canary Islands in 1880, where it is now established.

The Monarch migrates annually back and forth between the northern and southern parts of North America. Although its migratory habits allow it to distribute itself throughout the entire world, it can only become established where its food-plants (milkweeds, Asclepiadaceae particularly *Asclepias* spp.) grow; they are absent from Britain. Other species, which are strong fliers and well-known migrants are the Clouded Yellow, Painted Lady and Red Admiral (see pp. 118, 121), which are all widely distributed. These species fly up annually from North Africa and the Mediterranean countries to northern Europe where they are common in favourable years. Cabbage White butterflies (Large and Small Whites, *Pieris* spp., p. 114) also migrate, as does the smaller but fast-flying Long-tailed Blue (*Lampides boeticus*) (see p. 100), which is widely distributed over more southerly warm regions and flies up annually towards northern Europe.

Only recently have some of the over-wintering sites of the Monarch been found, in remote parts of Mexico. The aggregation of thousands upon thousands of these butterflies in one small area is one of the most remarkable and dramatic phenomena in the butterfly world.

Bogs and mosses

Butterflies of boggy ground in
conifer forests or in mosses in Britain,
southern Scandinavia and Denmark

C. palaeno

Colias palaeno *Moorland Clouded Yellow*

The bogs of conifer forests are the typical biotope for this Clouded Yellow which is relatively common in northern Europe but does not occur in the British Isles. It is a fast and strong flier, which is why it is also encountered outside bogs, particularly in the tussocky meadows of northern Europe. In the far north and in the mountains the butterflies are somewhat smaller than the southern Swedish and Danish examples, which are nearer in size to those of central Europe, where the butterfly has a yellow upper surface (ssp. *europome*). The discal spot may be somewhat less distinct, and the dark edge to the wing more or less white-powdered. This single-brooded species flies in June and July. The caterpillar feeds on bog-whortleberry (*Vaccinium uliginosum*).

C. palaeno

P. machaon

P. machaon

ssp. britannicus
♂

♂
ssp. machaon

Papilio machaon *Swallowtail*

This magnificent butterfly is a strong and elegant flyer, but it is not common in the northern part of its range. It is found only in the fens of the Norfolk Broads in Britain. Meadow flowers and garden blooms such as lilac are favourite sources of nectar. An attempt has recently been made to reintroduce the butterfly to Wicken Fen, Cambridgeshire, where it formerly occurred but finally died out in the 1950s. Such reintroductions, meticulously planned, are an important means of conservation, but should be attempted only by experts. The English subspecies has wider dark markings, and also differs ecologically from other races. The species flies for one generation in May–June; a second generation may be found occasionally in August in southern Scandinavia, in Denmark and in England. The caterpillar feeds only on milk-parsley (*Peucedenum palustre*) in England but on other umbelliferous plants abroad. (Additional illustration on p. 81.)

B. ino

underside of hind-wing
×1.5

Brenthis ino *Lesser Marbled Fritillary*

This species is found quite commonly in Scandinavian meadows, glades, mosses and bogs, but does not occur in Britain. There is one generation in June and July. The ground colour of the female is somewhat lighter than that of the male. The larva feeds on cloudberry (*Rubus chamaemorus*) and meadowsweet (*Filipendula ulmaria*) as well as other plants.

Boloria aquilonaris *Cranberry Fritillary*

This butterfly is absent from the British Isles. It is commoner in northern Scandinavia than in the south. The northern ssp. *aquilonaris* is smaller and somewhat redder than ssp. *alethea* which flies in southern Sweden and Denmark. In mountainous regions the species is small, and finely patterned. It occurs in bogs, mosses and marshes. Because of its redder coloration and its more rapid wing movements, it is often possible to distinguish it from other fritillaries, even in flight. There is a single generation in June and July. The caterpillar feeds on cranberry (*Vaccinium oxycoccus*).

B. aquilonaris

ssp. alethea

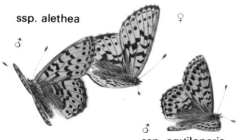

underside
of hind-wing
×1.5

ssp. aquilonaris

♀ u
♂

C. freija

Clossiana freija   *Freyja's Fritillary*

This is one of the earliest butterflies to appear on the northern Scandinavian bogs. The species is absent from the British Isles and rare in southern Sweden but occurs commonly in the north. Two other fritillary species which are very similar to *C. freija* fly in the Scandinavian mountains, but in the bogs of the conifer forest the underside of *C. freija* is quite unlike that of other species with which it flies. The sexes are outwardly similar. There is a single generation which flies from May to July. The caterpillar is believed to feed on cloudberry (*Rubus chamaemorus*) and bog-whortleberry (*Vaccinium uliginosum*).

Species of small fritillaries are very characteristic of bogs in the northern conifer belts of Scandinavia. Six species fly at the same time beginning in mid-June: *Brenthis ino*; *Boloria aquilonaris, Clossiana euphrosyne, C. freija, C. frigga* and *Proclossiana eunomia*. The earliest species, *C. freija*, is often encountered in a very worn condition, when other species are fresh and bright, as it is often found at the end of May.

B. ino

B. aquilonaris

C. freija

23

♀ u

C. frigga

♀

Clossiana frigga *Frigga's Fritillary*

This rather rare butterfly flies over boggy and mossy ground in woodlands, but is also found in mountains, usually on marshy ground and often in areas where willows grow. It often flies in company with the Bog Fritillary and Pearl-bordered Fritillary. *C. frigga* flies close to the ground like these species, but is bigger, faster and more robust. The dark inner half and occasional extensive dark markings of the hind-wings and occasional extensive dark markings of the fore-wings make it appear dark in the field. The sexes have similar markings, but the female is usually larger than the male. The marking of the underside of the rear wings makes this species easy to distinguish from the other fritillaries. Frigga's Fritillary does not occur in the British Isles and only rarely in Scandinavia. There is a single short-lived generation during the period from early June to July. The caterpillar is believed to feed on cloudberry (*Rubus chamaemorus*).

Clossiana euphrosyne ♂
(see p. 87)

C. frigga

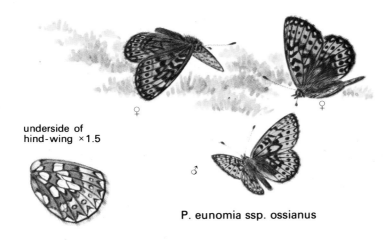

underside of
hind-wing ×1.5

♀

♀

♂

P. eunomia ssp. ossianus

Proclossiana eunomia *Bog Fritillary*

This is another European butterfly which does not occur in Britain. Three subspecies fly in northern Europe, all of which have white or shining silver spots on the underside of the hind-wings, while the central European form has yellow spots. The most northerly subspecies, *montana*, is small and light-coloured with sharp markings; it flies up to the treeline. Ssp. *ossianus*, found in boggy woodland areas, is larger than ssp. *montana* and has heavier markings—the females are darkly marked. Ssp. *subargentata* is found from central Sweden southwards; it is large and has a pale ground colouring with fine markings. The central European form is ssp. *eunomia*. The species is rare in bogs, but is more abundant in the far north where it is common in certain years. Like other small fritillaries in boggy areas, it flies low over tussocks of grass. The flight period is from June to July, and there is only a single generation annually. The caterpillar feeds on species of violet, particularly the marsh violet (*Viola palustris*), and on *Polygonum* spp.

P. eunomia

P. eunomia
ssp. subargentata
♀

25

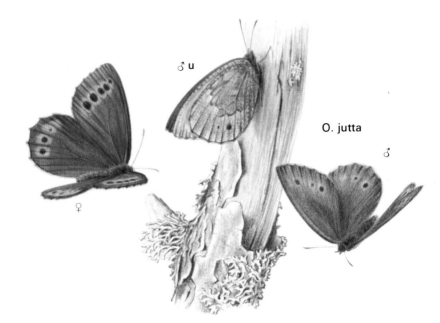

♂ u

O. jutta

♂

♀

Oeneis jutta   *Baltic Grayling*

Bogs with pine trees, and damp woodlands are the special haunt of this species. Quick in flight, it also likes to sit on the bark of pine trunks with wings closed; the underside markings then blend with the background—one frequently becomes aware of it only as it takes to the wing. Males can often be observed flying up and down one pine trunk and then another, presumably searching for females. Development takes two years because the caterpillar over-winters twice. The butterfly flies in June and July and is usually common in even-numbered years (e.g. 1980). The species is not found in the British Isles but occurs throughout the Baltic region; it is circumpolar and occurs in North America as far south as New England. The eye-markings of both sexes vary in number and size. The larva's host plant is not known.

O. jutta

E. embla

E. disa

26

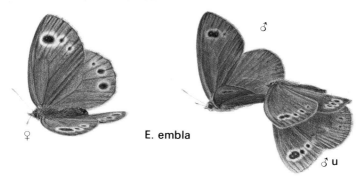

E. embla

Erebia embla *Lapland Ringlet*

A large dark butterfly that flutters among the pines one or two metres among Scandinavian bogs and mosses is a Lapland Ringlet. The patience of the butterfly collector is sorely tested when chasing this strong and evasive flyer in country where one sinks up to the knees in mossy water. The butterfly has a two-year life cycle, and flies sparingly in June–July. It does not occur in the British Isles. The wing markings are variable with the female's eye-spots generally lighter in colour and more widely distributed than in the male. The host plant of the caterpillar is unknown.

Erebia disa *Arctic Ringlet*

This species closely resembles *E. embla* but does not have eye-spots on the hind wings. The eyes on the front wings lie in a relatively straight line on a yellow-brown strip and are not as clearly ringed as in the Lapland Ringlet. The outer, somewhat lighter, half of the underside of the hind-wing also has a dark band which is missing from the Lapland Ringlet. Its flight is weaker than that of the latter species.

The Arctic Ringlet occurs only in the far north; it is not known south of latitude 64 S. Another circumpolar species, it is present in Canada as well as northern Scandinavia, but does not occur, of course, in the British Isles. A rare species, it flies for a short period in June and July. It occurs in high northern birch forests as well as pine woods. The foodplant of the caterpillar is not known.

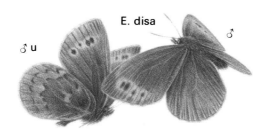

E. disa

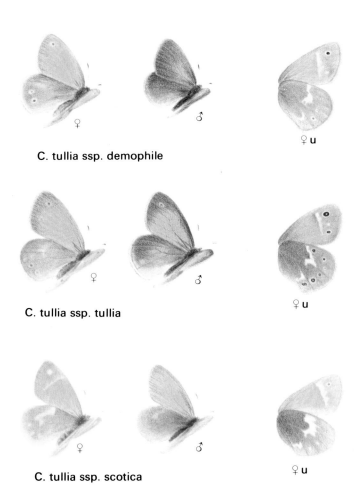

C. tullia ssp. demophile

C. tullia ssp. tullia

C. tullia ssp. scotica

Erebia epiphron *Mountain Ringlet*

This little grass butterfly is really a mountain species, but has been included here because it can be found at an altitude as low as 450 m. More usually, however, it flies at about 1,000 m over grassy or mossy ground. Although it is very localised it is found, in some places commonly, in Scotland and Cumbria as well as mountains in Europe (excluding Scandinavia). The male is darker than the female. The caterpillar feeds on mat-grass (*Nardus stricta*).

Coenonympha tullia *Large Heath*

This species exhibits distinct geographic variation; four subspecies can be recognised in northern Europe although they grade into one another and transitional forms are usual. All are single-brooded. The caterpillar feeds on beaked rush (*Rhynchospara alba*) and also on cotton-grass (*Eriophorum* spp.).

Coenonympha tullia rothliebii

The subspecies is found in bogs, mosses and occasionally in more grassy places. As a result of drainage work and land-reclamation it is being threatened in its limited area of distribution in north-western England (Shropshire, Lancashire and Cumbria). It resembles ssp. *tullia*, but the male has a darker, grey-brown upper surface and the hind-wings usually have three to five eye-spots. The underside of the fore-wings has two to four and the underside of the hind-wings six large eye-spots. The female is rather paler, with four or five eye-spots on the upper surface of the hind wings.

Coenonympha tullia tullia

Flies in similar areas as *C.t. rothliebii* during June and July, but only sometimes into August. It is found in Scotland south of about latitude 56 N, in northern England and in northern Wales. It also occurs in Denmark, southern Sweden and the Baltic region, grading into ssp. *demophile* further north.

Coenonympha tullia scotica

The Scottish race of Large Heath flies in late June and July over bogs and peatlands up to about 750 m above sea-level in northern Scotland, Argyll, the Hebrides and Orkney Islands.

Coenonympha tullia demophile

Occurs in bogs of the northern Scandinavian conifer region and grades into ssp. *tullia* further south. The flight period is late June and July.

**E. epiphron
ssp. mnemon**
♀

E. epiphron

C. tullia

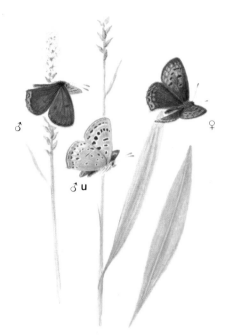

♂ ♂ u ♀

L. helle

Lycaena helle *Violet Copper*

Marshy meadows, damp areas along the edges of woods, mossy ground and bogs
are the places where the Violet Copper can be located. It is local in occurrence
but is sometimes found in large numbers, although not in Britain. The central
European specimens are paler than the more northerly ones. The female's
appearance varies considerably; in particular the orange markings of the fore-wings
may show up more or less prominently—the female illustrated here has extensive
orange markings. She differs from the male by her lack of violet lustre on the
upperside of the wings. This strong violet coloration of the male appears only under
certain angles of lighting, while at other angles the wing has a more yellowy-brown
tone. This butterfly is quite unusual. It is single-brooded and is on the wing from the
end of May until the beginning of July. The caterpillar feeds on knot-grass and
sorrel (*Polygonum* and *Rumex*).

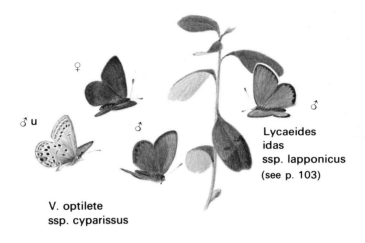

♀

♂ u

♂

♂

Lycaeides
idas
ssp. lapponicus
(see p. 103)

V. optilete
ssp. cyparissus

Vacciniina optilete *Cranberry Blue*

Bogs and marshes are the usual habitats of this butterfly, but it also flies in pine forests where cowberry is abundant. It is absent from the British Isles and less common in the southern part of Scandinavia, where it can be found over mossy ground. In other places it is quite common. In northern Scandinavia the subspecies *cyparissus* has been recognised; this race is smaller than the typical one and the dark edge of the male is narrower. Otherwise there is little variation. Occasionally the female has a small orange spot on the upper surface of the hind-wing. Single-brooded, it flies from the end of June until the beginning of August. The caterpillar feeds on cowberry, bog whortleberry and cranberry, all species of *Vaccinium*.

L. helle

V. optilete

31

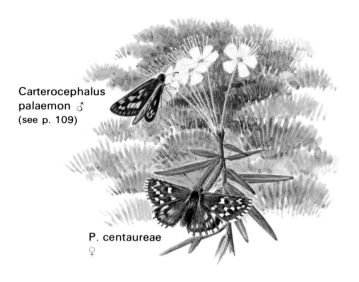

Carterocephalus
palaemon ♂
(see p. 109)

P. centaureae
♀

Pyrgus centaureae *Northern Grizzled Skipper*

This is a relatively large Skipper which flies mainly over boggy and mossy ground, but occasionally in damp meadows and woodland. It darts so rapidly that it is difficult to spot and follow, but it will suddenly settle on a leaf with wings outspread, displaying its distinctive pattern. The Northern Grizzled Skipper is not found in the British Isles but occurs throughout northern Scandinavia. It is single-brooded and flies in June and July. The sexes are similarly marked. The caterpillar feeds on cloudberry (*Rubus chamaemorus*).

There are several similar species: the Alpine Grizzled Skipper (*P. andromedae*) which flies in the higher parts of the birch belt in the mountains and above the treeline (not illustrated), and the Large Grizzled Skipper (p. 78) which do not have the pale spots on the upper surface of the hind-wings. The Grizzled Skipper (p. 108) is smaller and lacks the pale veins on the underside of the hind-wings of the Northern Grizzled Skipper.

P. centaureae

Woods, parks and scrub

Butterflies which are found in woodland glades and along woodland tracks, or among trees and bushes at the edges of woods and on wooded grazing land

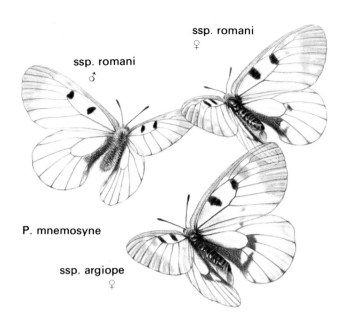

ssp. romani
♀

ssp. romani
♂

P. mnemosyne

ssp. argiope
♀

Parnassius mnemosyne *Clouded Apollo*

The Clouded Apollo, like its near relative the Apollo, readily forms local races. No fewer than nine subspecies have been described in northern Europe, which means that there is one in almost every area where the butterfly is found. Two of these are illustrated here, ssp. *romani* which flies in the Uppland province of Sweden and ssp. *argiope* from southern Sweden. The nominate form flies in southern Finland and closely resembles ssp. *romani*. The Scandinavian forms of the Clouded Apollo are some of the most distinctly marked and have an almost pure white ground colour. The butterfly is a mountain species in central and southern Europe, and is smaller and more darkly marked. It is not found in the British Isles and is very local and usually rare in Scandinavia, but in some years it can be quite plentiful. The very few sightings in Norway have been at altitudes up to 700 m above sea level. Otherwise it favours coastal areas and lush, flowery and often damp woodland pasture surrounded by trees and shrubs.

Its flight is similar to that of the Apollo—an elegant glide between bushes 2–3 m above the ground and an occasional flutter close to the ground with wings almost vibrating. Usually, however, the flight is rather clumsy and its appearance tends to be greyish, especially the female. At rest it often sits among clumps of meadowsweet or other plants, and is then difficult to spot. This single-brooded species flies from the end of May until the beginning of July. The caterpillar feeds on members of the Fumitory family (*Corydalis*).

34

A. crataegi

Aporia crataegi   *Black-veined White*

A rather large white butterfly, with a similar flight to the Apollo, the Black-veined White in found in lightly wooded and grazing areas and in clearings, often near water. It became extinct in the British Isles in the 1920s. It is found in Denmark (principally in eastern Jutland) and in southern Sweden. In some years the butterfly is quite common and occurs in large numbers, but in others it is rare. The differences between the sexes are in the colours of the wing veins; black in the male and brownish in the female. The female also has very sparse scaling so that her wings look almost transparent. The Black-veined White has one generation a year and flies in June and July. The caterpillar feeds on hawthorn (*Crataegus* spp.), plum, blackthorn (*Prunus* spp.) and is sometimes a fruit-tree pest.

P. mnemosyne

A. crataegi

35

Gonepteryx rhamni *Brimstone*

This is one of our best known species. Its lemon-yellow colouring brightens up the dull wood when winter is over. The Brimstone is one of the hibernating butterflies—it over-winters among evergreens, including ivy or in other sheltered places. In late summer newly emerged Brimstones look for nectar on many different kinds of flowers in open places as well as in woodland rides and clearings. Then they may linger all through the autumn, and be found even on warm, sunny days in midwinter. The last of the hibernated individuals may fly as late as midsummer; this makes the Brimstone perhaps our longest-lived species. After hibernation it flies in woodland areas and takes nectar from spring flowers and blossoming sallow. Mating takes place at this time; the female lays her eggs on buckthorn (*Rhamnus cathartica*) or Alder Blackthorn (*Frangula alnus*) which are the foodplants of the caterpillar. (See also p. 45.)

♂

Pieris napi
(see p. 116)

G. rhamni

♀

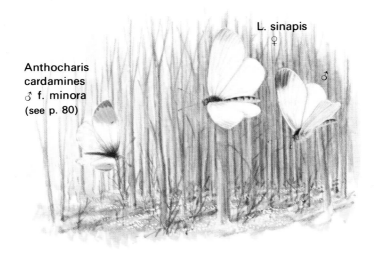

L. sinapis
♀

♂

Anthocharis cardamines ♂ f. minora (see p. 80)

Leptidea sinapis   *Wood White*

The Wood White, with its weak fluttering flight, is one of the most delicate butterflies, and is immediately distinguished from other, more powerful white species with which it appears in the spring. The first generation flies in May and June. A second generation appears in some years in parts of England, but is even more sporadic further north. The second-generation males usually have a smaller, more rounded and darker marking on the apex of the fore-wing, while the female's is paler or almost absent. The species is usually found in wooded areas, where it flies in glades, along rides or at woodland edges; in parts of Ireland it inhabits more open areas. A rare find in eastern England, it is more common, though local, in the west. The caterpillar feeds on leguminous plants, particularly meadow vetchling (*Lathyrus pratensis*). Species of white butterflies, superficially similar to Wood White, are illustrated on p. 117.

C. rhamni

L. sinapis

L. camilla   ♀

Limenitis camilla   *White Admiral*

This fine butterfly occurs locally in woods where the larval foodplant honeysuckle (*Lonicera periclymenum*) grows. In sunny, hot years it is able to extend its range, as it did throughout southern England in the early 1940s. It glides elegantly and expertly among tree branches and likes to visit brambles in flower. The White Admiral is single-brooded and flies from late June until the end of July. The sexes are similar in appearance. The caterpillar constructs a special 'hibernaculum' in which it over-winters.

Limenitis populi   *Poplar Admiral*

The Popular Admiral is found rather rarely in Swedish woods where aspen grows, but is locally common in certain years. It does not occur in Britain. Most of its time is spent among the treetops so that observations can be made only occasionally when it descends to drink in puddles of water in forest rides. It does not visit flowers, but is attracted to mammal excrement. There is a single annual generation with flight in late June and July. The caterpillar feeds on aspen and poplars (*Populus* spp.).

L. camilla

L. populi

38

L. populi

♂ u

♀

♂

♀

♂ u

♂

A. iris

Apatura iris *Purple Emperor*

Like the Poplar Admiral, the Purple Emperor, found locally in southern England, spends most of its time in the treetops and only comes down to the ground to drink or when attracted by excrement or rotting meat. Very occasionally it visits a flowering bramble or sap oozing from a treetrunk. The habitat is in woodland, usually where there is oak. The male's purple lustre is an example of 'structural colours' produced by light refraction from the wing-scales and is seen only at certain angles. Like the Poplar Admiral, the female is larger, flies more slowly and descends more often to low levels. The butterflies frequently congregate around the top of a particular 'master tree'. The Purple Emperor is single-brooded and flies in July and August. The well-camouflaged caterpillar feeds on goat willow and other sallows (*Salix* spp.).

N. antiopa ♀

Nymphalis antiopa *Camberwell Beauty*

The large dark Camberwell Beauty flies in wooded country where it often sits on bare soil to absorb the sun's heat. Its flight is quick and sure. It rarely visits flowers, but is attracted to sap running from trees and to rotting fruit. In the late summer of plentiful years large numbers may gather on a birch with running sap and stay for several days before looking for a suitable place to hibernate. Populations vary considerably from year to year, but reach a peak about every tenth year when it is then locally common. Between these peaks the butterfly is rare; it may even seem to disappear completely. It is found only occasionally in the British Isles, although a notably numerous migration to Britain occurred in 1976. There is one generation a year, the adults flying from the beginning of August, and again from April to June following hibernation. The yellow borders of the wings fade to pale yellow or white during hibernation (see pp. 4 and 45). The caterpillar feeds on sallows and willows (*Salix* spp.) and also on birch (*Betula* spp.).

A. iris

N. antiopa

41

N. polychloros

Nymphalis polychloros *Large Tortoiseshell*

At first glance this butterfly may look very much like the common Small Tortoise-shell, but it is so different in character that confusion is unlikely. The Large Tortoiseshell is rather large, quick and remarkably shy and frequently sits on tree-trunks with wings closed or on bare ground with wings outspread. As it darts away the colour seems to be yellow-brown; this is more like the impression given by a Comma (p. 44) than by the red and yellow of the Small Tortoiseshell. The Large Tortoiseshell does not visit flowers except for trees in blossom, but, like the Camberwell Beauty, it is often found where there is sap exuding from trees. After it emerges at the end of July it flies for only a few days before starting midsummer hibernation in a stone wall or hollow tree. The best opportunity for observation is when spring arrives and, together with other hibernating species, it flies along woodland ridges and the edges of woods (see p. 45). Populations have drastically declined during the last few decades and it is considered rare in most places. Dutch elm disease, which has destroyed many elm trees (*Ulmus* spp.), is undoubtedly the reason why the species is now extremely uncommon in England. This is because elms are the usual diet for the caterpillars. They have been known, however, to feed on other types of trees.

N. xanthomelas   Aglais urticae   N. vaualbum
                   (see p. 122)

(see p. 122)

Nymphalis xanthomelas   *Yellow-legged Tortoiseshell*

This is an eastern Europe species which temporarily established itself in Sweden in the 1950s and 1960s and which has occurred once or twice in Britain and Denmark as a very rare vagrant. The Yellow-legged Tortoiseshell and Large Tortoiseshell are very similar: apart from the differences shown in the illustrations, the Yellow-legged has light yellowy-brown legs, while the Large has dark ones. There is one brood a year with the butterflies on the wing from July to September, and again in the spring after hibernation. The caterpillar usually feeds on sallows and willows (*Salix* spp.).

Nymphalis vaualbum   *False Comma*

This is an eastern species, like the Yellow-legged Tortoiseshell, which is occasionally found in Denmark, Sweden, Finland and the Baltic, probably only as vagrant specimens. It is single-brooded flying from July to September and again in the spring after hibernation. The caterpillar feeds mainly on elms, birches, and poplars (*Ulmus*, *Betula* and *Populus* spp.).

N. polychloros   *N. xanthomelas*   *N. vaualbum*

♀ u

P. c-album

♂

♂ u

Polygonia c-album *Comma*

Commas can be found along woodland ridges and paths, at the corners of woods and in small glades where they sit on the ground, a low leaf or a branch. There are two generations; the first, f. *hutchinsoni*, is lighter in colour, emerges in June and is only partial even in England and does not appear every year in northern Europe. The second generation emerges at the end of July and hibernates. During hibernation its 'tattered' outline is very similar to a dead leaf. The Latin name of the species comes from the single white markings on the underside of each of the hind-wings. The caterpillar lives on stinging nettle (*Urtica dioica*) and hop (*Humulus lupulus*) as well as various trees and shrubs.

P. c-album

In a typical Scandinavian woodland the first of the season's butterflies, the hibernating species, are enticed out by the spring sunshine, even before the trees burst into leaf. Among them are Camberwell Beauty, Large Tortoiseshell, Comma, Small Tortoiseshell, Peacock and Brimstone.

A. levana

2nd gen. (f. prorsa)
♀

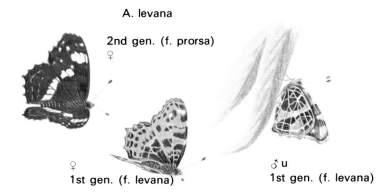

♀
1st gen. (f. levana)

♂ u
1st gen. (f. levana)

Araschnia levana   *Map Butterfly*

The Map Butterfly is local and uncommon in Denmark and also throughout the Baltic as far as south-eastern Finland. It was once introduced into England, but later exterminated. It has a striking seasonal dimorphism, i.e. the two generations are very different in appearance. The first (f. *levana*) flies in May and June and resembles a fritillary while the second (f. *prorsa*) flies in July and August and looks like a miniature White Admiral (p. 38). Intermediate forms are rather common. The male's wing is more pointed than the female's. The caterpillar feeds on stinging nettle (*Urtica dioica*).

The many fritillary species (below) that prefer wooded areas fly in glades and nectar on flowering herbs and shrubs (see pp. 83–7).

♂ u

E. maturna

♀

♂

Euphydryas maturna *Scarce Fritillary*

This pretty fritillary, not found in the British Isles, is local and rare in wooded areas of southern Fennoscandia, particularly in damp valley-bottoms or in marshes where ash grows. It is found in sheltered glades where it spins down to settle among the tree leaves or on meadowsweet. A fast flier, it often simply dashes by and disappears over the treetops. The butterfly is single-brooded and flies during the latter half of June. The caterpillars live together before hibernation in a communal nest of silk which is usually spun among ash leaves (*Fraxinus excelsior*). After hibernation the larvae feed singly on various herbs.

A. levana

E. maturna

47

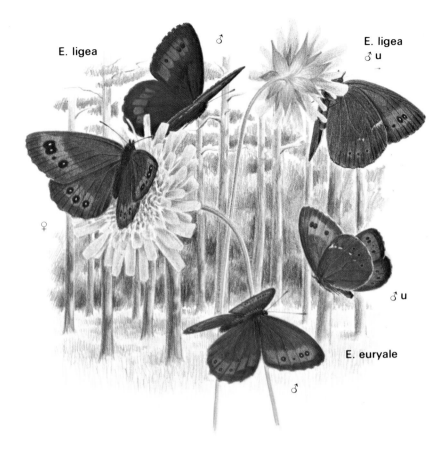

Erebia ligea   *Arran Brown*

Although not regarded as a British species, one or two specimens have been taken in Scotland and Arran Brown may yet prove to be native here. It flies commonly in flowery places in woods, in glades and along woodland rides throughout Scandinavia. Development takes two years—the uneven-numbered ones have proved best. It flies in July and August. The caterpillar feeds on various grasses.

Erebia euryale   *Large Ringlet*

This species flies in uneven years in south-eastern Finland (as ssp. *euryaloides*) but not in the British Isles. It is similar to Arran Brown but the male lacks the patches of scent scales. Grasses are the diet of the caterpillars.

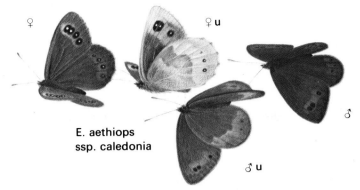

E. aethiops
ssp. caledonia

Erebia aethiops   *Scotch Argus*

Two forms of this species fly in the British Isles: f. *caledonia* occurs in southern and western Scotland as far as central Perthshire, and f. *aethiops* to the north of this area and in northern England. Whether f. *caledonia* is a distinct subspecies is doubtful but it is smaller than the nominate form. Also, the orange band is distinctly constricted in the middle and it has, on average, fewer eye-spots—the male rarely more than three on the upperside of the fore-wing. A sun-lover, it is found in grassy, open wooded country and at the edges of woods. It is single-brooded and flight is in July and August. The caterpillar feeds on various grasses.

Erebia embla and O. jutta, see pp. 26–7.

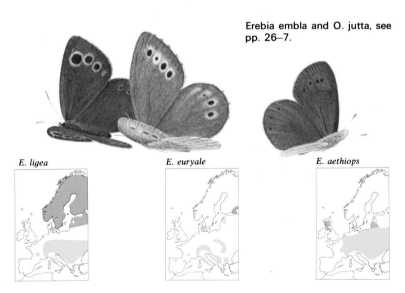

E. ligea   E. euryale   E. aethiops

♂ ssp. tircis

♀ u ssp. tircis

♀ ssp. oblita

P. aegeria

Pararge aegeria   *Speckled Wood*

Speckled Wood has two generations in the British Isles—May and June and
August—and three in some long, hot summers. The habitat is deciduous woodlands,
where it frequents rides, glades and grassy areas. In central Scandinavia there is a
single generation in June–July which is found in sparse pine forests. Individuals
are difficult to follow in flight because of their rather jerky movements in and out
of shafts of sunlight and shadows of trees and bushes. Males defend small patches
of sunlight as 'territories' and it is very usual to see one spinning into a glade
from a height of a few metres to sit on a sunlit leaf, only to throw itself after an
intruding butterfly and spiral upwards in a wild chase the very next moment.
The female is somewhat larger than the male, with lighter and larger spots. The
second generation is somewhat darker than the first. In Scotland, where the species
is uncommon but spreading, the subspecies *oblita* has developed in the Western
Isles; it is dark with large, pale, almost white, spots (the female is illustrated).
The British and Scandinavian subspecies is *tircis*, which has pale yellow spots.
The nominate form, with orange spots, flies in southern Europe. The caterpillar
feeds on various common grasses.

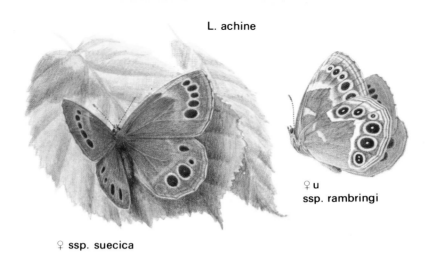

♀ u
ssp. rambringi

♀ ssp. suecica

Lopinga achine *Woodland Brown*

Widely distributed, although in scattered colonies, throughout central and eastern Europe, this species does not occur in the British Isles and has become rare and very local in southern Sweden. The Woodland Brown still occurs, as ssp. *suecica*, in open deciduous woodland on the mainland—Ostergotland. As late as 1949 the species was discovered on the island of Gotland, where it flies in grassy, pine forests which have a proportion of deciduous trees and bushes. These butterflies, ssp. *rambringi*, are protected in Gotland; as always, collectors should respect regulations made for the conservation of nationally rare or very local species and subspecies.

As it flutters weakly in the woodland understorey or glides gently among the leaves in a glade, the butterfly appears to be pale grey in colour. The males emerge during the first few days of July, well before the females, which appear about a week later. The female is somewhat larger and paler. The caterpillar lives on various species of grasses.

P. aegeria

L. achine

51

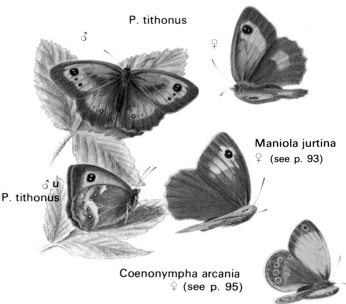

P. tithonus

♂

♀

P. tithonus ♂u

Maniola jurtina
♀ (see p. 93)

Coenonympha arcania
♀ (see p. 95)

Pyronia tithonus *Gatekeeper*

The Gatekeeper, or Hedge Brown, is a high summer species which flies in July and August along the edges of woods, around clumps of bushes in grassland and especially near hedges. Visits to brambles are frequent, as the butterflies nectar freely on the flowers. Females emerge rather later than males. This species somewhat resembles the Meadow Brown, especially ssp. *splendida*, which has a similar orange-brown ground colour on the upper side of the hind-wings, but is always easily identified by its underside. The male illustrated here has two dark spots beneath the eye-spots of the fore-wings which are normally missing. However, individual variants with one or two such spots are not unusual. A generally common species in England, Wales and southern Ireland, it is extinct in Scotland. The caterpillar feeds on various grasses.

Lasiommata
maera
♂ (see p. 64)

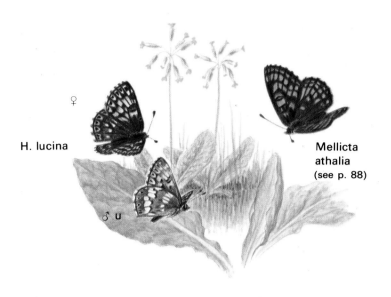

♀

H. lucina

Mellicta
athalia
(see p. 88)

♂ u

Hamearis lucina   *Duke of Burgundy Fritillary*

A local but not rare species in southern England, it has disappeared from some
localities here and from others in Denmark and Scandinavia. It is the only
European representative of the family Nemeobiidae, which has many species in the
tropics, especially South America. The Duke of Burgundy Fritillary, which
resembles a small fritillary, had a rapid, darting flight, somewhat similar to that of
many skippers. It flies in May and June and is usually single-brooded, although
occasional examples of a second generation have been found in August and
September. Variation is very slight. The female is generally slightly larger and
has more rounded and ample wings than the male. The butterfly is found in
woodland glades along woodland rides and in grassland near woods where the
larval foodplants cowslip and primrose (*Primula veris* and *P. vulgaris*) are plentiful.

P. tithonus

H. lucina

Q. quercus

Quercusia quercus *Purple Hairstreak*

The Purple Hairstreak is not often seen except when it flies around the tops of oaks and other trees. It rarely visits flowers but will occasionally descend onto a clump of bushes or young trees to feed on the honeydew of greenfly. Because of the habits of the adult, Purple Hairstreak is easy to overlook; but it is quite common in oak woods; it is usually easier to find the eggs and caterpillars than the adults. The eggs are laid on oak twigs, near the buds, and the caterpillars, usually described as 'woodlouse-shaped', greatly resemble the bud-scales of the host tree. There is one generation a year, with the butterflies emerging in July.

Q. quercus

T. betulae

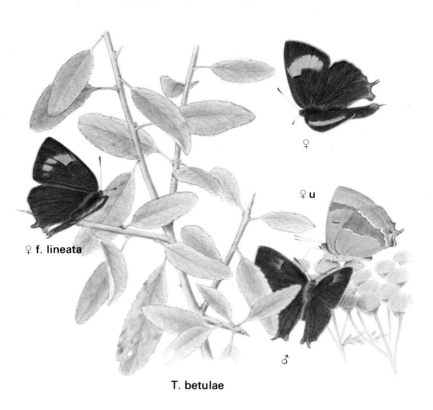

♀

♀ u

♀ f. lineata

♂

T. betulae

Thecla betulae   *Brown Hairstreak*

The name of this species is misleading, because the caterpillar feeds on blackthorn (*Prunus spinosa*) rather than birch (*Betula* spp.). It is a late summer butterfly which seldom emerges before the middle of August, but occasionally as early as the end of July. It continues to fly into September or even October. It is found at the edges of woods and in hedges where blackthorn flourishes, and usually on clay soils. The adult is seldom seen, perhaps partly because it flies so late in the year, and the species is most easily found as the egg, relatively conspicuous on blackthorn twigs before the leaves appear. Young bushes are preferred by egg-laying females. The Brown Hairstreak occurs as very sparse and dispersed colonies, with neither adults nor early stages found in large numbers. It is widely distributed in southern England, Ireland and southern Scandinavia, but is considered scarce.

N. ilicis
♀
♂

S. pruni
♀

♂

S. pruni

♀
S. w-album

♂

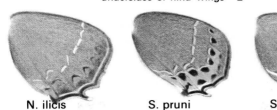

undersides of hind-wings ×2

N. ilicis   S. pruni   S. w-album

Nordmannia ilicis   *Ilex Hairstreak*

The Ilex Hairstreak does not occur in the British Isles and only rarely in Denmark and southern Sweden. It inhabits places with young oaks and brambles in flower. The butterfly is single-brooded, flying in July and the beginning of August. The caterpillar feeds on oaks (*Quercus* spp.), usually the young trees.

Strymonidia pruni   *Black Hairstreak*

There are about fifty colonies of the Black Hairstreak in wooded areas of the south-eastern Midlands of England. It has attracted much attention from conservationists, but is not now considered to be endangered. The butterflies visit flowers, particularly privet and the earliest brambles, and fly in late June and July in a single brood. The caterpillar feeds on blackthorn (*Prunus spinosa*) usually on sheltered, large, mature bushes.

Strymonidia w-album   *White-letter Hairstreak*

Threatened by the destruction of its foodplant by Dutch Elm disease in England, this already local species is likely to become rarer. It inhabits deciduous woods, parks, gardens and avenues of elms. The butterflies frequently fly among the tops of tall trees, but come down to visit thistles and bramble bushes. The white 'W' marking on the underside of the hind-wings gives the species its name. It is single-brooded, flying in July and August. The caterpillar feed on several elm (*Ulmus* spp.) species.

N. ilicis

S. pruni

S. w-album

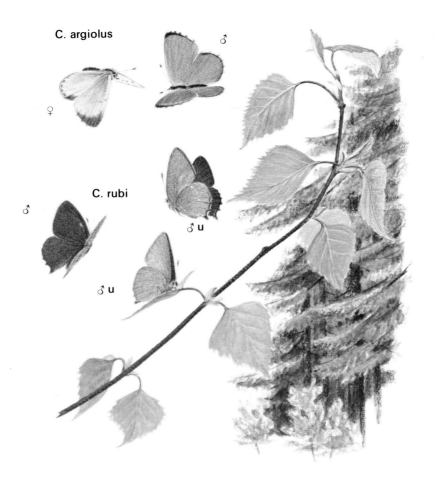

C. argiolus

♂

♀

C. rubi

♂

♂ u

♂ u

Callophrys rubi *Green Hairstreak*

This is our commonest Hairstreak, a flyer over many kinds of ground, including the edges of woods, glades, heaths and moorland. The butterfly frequently sits on the leaves of young trees and bushes with the undersides of the wings almost exactly matching the background. After a quick but usually short flight the butterfly settles on a leaf with closed wings and turns around to find the best position for absorbing the sun's warmth. One of the earliest butterflies to emerge in the spring, it flies in a single brood from the end of April to June. The male is most easily distinguished from the female by the patches of scent-scales at the edge of the discal cell on the upperside of his fore-wings. The white spotted lines of the underside vary in extent. The Green Hairstreak occurs throughout the British Isles, except the Orkneys and Shetlands, and over most of Scandinavia. The caterpillar is more or less polyphagous (feeds on many different plants). The over-wintering stage is the pupa.

G. alexis
ssp. schneideri

♀

♂

G. alexis
ssp. schneideri ♂ u

C. argiolus ♂ u

Glaucopsyche alexis *Green-underside Blue*

This Blue does not occur in the British Isles and is rare in southern Sweden. It is often encountered singly and flies one or two metres above the ground. It is found at the edges of woods and in wooded grazing land. There is a single generation in June and July. Ssp. *schneideri* has been distinguished in Scandinavia; the spots on the underside of the hind-wings are smaller, and the blue-green shade of the wing-bases is lighter than in ssp. *alexis*. The caterpillar feeds on common melilot (*Melilotus officinalis*) and other Leguminosae.

Celastrina argiolus *Holly Blue*

This, the first Blue of the season, occurs in gardens, along woodland rides and in glades, and often flies several metres above the ground. The Holly Blue only occasionally visits flowers but sometimes drinks at damp patches on the ground. It is generally common, but has intervals of several years when it is scarce. There are two generations in the British Isles, in April and May, and July and August; second-brood butterflies have darker markings. Females have more extensive black upperside markings than males in both broods. The caterpillar feeds on the flowers and fruits of several trees and shrubs, especially holly (*Ilex aquifolium*) and ivy (*Hedera helix*).

C. rubi

C. argiolus

G. alexis

59

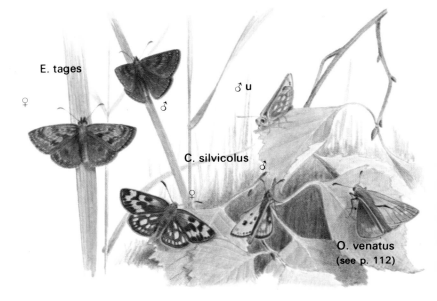

E. tages

♀

♂ u

♂

C. silvicolus

♂

♀

O. venatus
(see p. 112)

Erynnis tages *Dingy Skipper*

The first Skipper of the season is found at the edges of woods, in glades, on embankments, in sheltered downland hollows and similar areas where its larval foodplant bird's-foot trefoil (*Lotus corniculatus*) grows. This sun-loving butterfly is often seen on the ground or on low-growing plants with its wings outspread. It is single-brooded, flying in May and June, with a rare second generation in southern England. It is common in England and parts of Scotland.

Carterocephalus silvicolus *Northern Chequered Skipper*

The haunts of this species, which closely resembles the Chequered Skipper (see p. 109), are places where flowers grow, preferably rather damp woodland glades and the edges of bogs. It is absent from the British Isles, fairly common in Finland and rare or local elsewhere. There is a single generation in June and July. The larva feeds on various grasses.

E. tages

C. silvicolus

Mountainous and stony ground

Butterflies of mountainsides, coastal areas, bushy open ground, sparsely wooded grazing land or stony grassland with stone walls

♀ u

♂

S. orion

♀

Scolitantides orion *Chequered Blue*

This butterfly flies in a single generation at the end of May and June on chalky, stony or rocky ground. It does not occur in Britain and is rare in southern Scandinavia. This area is widely separated from southern Europe, where the butterfly also occurs. The caterpillar feeds on species of stonecrop (*Sedum* spp.). The Baton Blue is a similar, but smaller, species and less heavily marked on the underside (see p. 74).

Parnassius apollo *Apollo Butterfly*

This is one of the species, once quite common, which has disappeared from many areas in the last few decades; however, it has never been found in the British Isles. It still flies quite commonly on Gotland as ssp. *linnaei*, which is somewhat smaller than the mainland form. The butterfly is a lowland species in the Finnish and Swedish archipelagos but elsewhere in Europe inhabits hilly, mountainous and thinly wooded ground. The butterfly is normally somewhat clumsy on the wing but its movements can change to an elegant glide as it soars along mountain ridges and on to clumps of thistle in the valley below.

During mating a parchment-like pouch (sphragis) is formed beneath the abdomen of the female. Few species vary as much as Apollo, and a confusing large number of 'subspecies' and forms have been described. The female illustrated is an extreme and rare variant found in Gotland. The flight period is June and July with a single generation. The larva lives on species of stonecrop (*Sedum* spp.).

S. orion

P. apollo

P. apollo ssp. linnaei ab.

♀

♂

P. apollo ssp. linnaei

♀

P. apollo ssp. apollo

L. megera

Lasiommata megera *Wall Brown*

Warm and dry places such as gravel pits, bare pathways, stone walls and other open areas are the favourite haunt of this distinctive sun-lover which less commonly visits flowers. Its flight is generally jerky and short. Common in England, Wales and Ireland, it flies in two broods, in May and June and from the end of July to September. The caterpillar feeds on various common grass species.

Lasiommata maera *Large Wall Brown*

Common throughout most of Europe except the British Isles, this is a fairly large dark species. Its fluttering flight is occasionally interrupted by swifter glides as it flies over bare ground and along dry stone walls. It sometimes visits meadow flowers. Although it prefers stony ground, it may also be encountered on roadsides, sparse woodland and other dry places. There is a single generation, the adults flying from June to August. The larva feeds on various common grasses, particularly annual meadow-grass (*Poa annua*). In northern Europe the Large Wall Brown is easily distinguished from the Wall Brown by its darker colour; in southern Europe it is much more orange.

L. megera

L. maera

L. petropolitana

L. petropolitaria

L. maera

Lasiommata petropolitana *Northern Wall Brown*

Found in the same places, this species closely resembles the Large Wall Brown.
However, it can always be distinguished by the markings of the upper surface:
the fore-wings, and the middle of the hind-wings, have distinct dark lines running
through them and a bow-shaped dark line that parallels the outer edge of the wing.
It flies earlier than the Large Wall Brown, usually in May and June, but the
time varies with latitude. The butterfly is absent from the British Isles but occurs
quite commonly in dry stony woodland in Scandinavia. The larva feeds on various
grasses.

H. alcyone
ssp. norvegica

♀

♂ u

H. semele
♀ u
(see p. 73)

Hipparchia alcyone *Rock Grayling*

This species does not occur in the British Isles, nor in most of Scandinavia, but it flies in southern Norway as ssp. *norvegica*, which is smaller and darker than the central European nominate form. This isolated population may be considered as a survival from warmer times. The habitat is mountainous and rocky south-facing slopes, often with scattered conifer trees. The rapid flight over this terrain makes it difficult to catch. It resembles the Grayling (p. 73) in its flight and habit of sitting on bare ground and treetrunks. The male is usually somewhat smaller than the female; his fore-wing is more pointed and has narrower and less extensive pale stripes. The butterfly flies as a single generation in July. The larva feeds on grasses, particularly tor-grass (*Brachypodium pinnatum*).

H. alcyone

Arid grassland

Butterflies found on poor, sandy
or dry grasslands, particularly
downs and limestone hills

♂ u   ♂   ♀

P. daplidice

Pontia daplidice   *Bath White*

This species is seen only occasionally in northern Europe; it is, however, markedly migratory and found in reasonable numbers in some years. Its occurrence is very uncertain in the British Isles—1945 was a particularly prolific year. The butterfly is resident in the island of Gotland, but elsewhere in Scandinavia it occurs only as a migrant and occasionally reaches central Sweden. The first specimen known to have been taken in England was caught in May 1702 and is still preserved in the J.C. Dale collection. This sun-loving rapid flyer thrives on arid ground, especially in coastal regions, but may also be encountered in clover and lucerne fields together with Clouded Yellows and Cabbage Whites. There are two generations each year in May and from July to September. The less numerous butterflies of the first generation are smaller and distinguished as f. *bellidice*. The green marking of the undersides of the wings is similar to that of the Orange Tip (p. 80). Green pigments are uncommon in the lepidoptera; the colours of these species are produced by a mixture of yellow and black wing-scales which is perceived as green by the human eye. Bath White caterpillars feed on various plants of the cabbage family (Cruciferae) and on wild mignonette (*Reseda lutea*).

P. daplidice

F. niobe

F. niobe   ♂

♀

Fabriciana niobe *Niobe Fritillary*

This butterfly resembles the High Brown Fritillary, but is smaller and does not occur in the British Isles. Like the High Brown Fritillary, it may or may not have silver underside markings on the hind-wings. *F. niobe*, which has the silver spots, is the more usual form in northern Europe, but elsewhere f. *eris*, without the spots, is more common. The two forms of both fritillaries may be distinguished by detailed examination of the undersides of the hind-wings (see below). The Niobe Fritillary is single-brooded and flies in July and August in more open areas than the High Brown species. The caterpillar feeds on violets (*Viola spp.*).

The Niobe Fritillary has a dark wing base and a pale spot in the discal area which often has a dark centre. The High Brown Fritillary does not usually have this spot; if it does, the centre is never dark. Cells 4–6 (see p. 8) have dark markings close to the discal area in *F. niobe*, but these are missing in *F. adippe*. Also in *F. adippe* the marginal spots are rounded, while in *F. niobe* they are angular, and its dark marginal stripe is distinct.

undersides of
hind-wings ×1.5

F. niobe f. niobe   F. adippe f. adippe

F. niobe f. eris   F. adippe f. cleodoxa

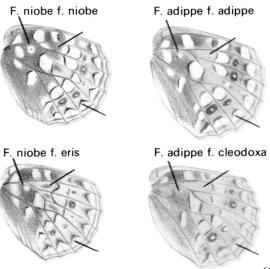

I. lathonia

Issoria lathonia *Queen of Spain Fritillary*

Rarely found in the British Isles, this is one of the earliest fritillaries of the season in Scandinavia. It is found on arid ground, where it rests with wings outspread, on bare earth or on pathways. It flies in two generations; the first in May and June, and the second, which is more numerous, from the end of July to September. The butterflies in the northern part of its range are comparatively small, while those in southern Sweden, Denmark and England are the same size as central European examples. A well-known migrant, it is found in England only as a visitor from the south. Its flight is powerful and quick, often close to the ground. Its movements have some of the same jerkiness characteristic of the Wall Brown (p. 64), with which it frequently flies in company. The caterpillar feeds on various violets (*Viola* spp.).

Clossiana euphrosyne
(see p. 87)

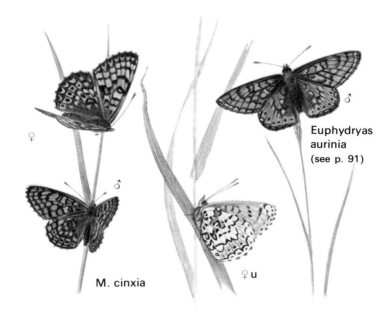

♀

Euphydryas
aurinia
(see p. 91)

♂

♂

M. cinxia

♀ u

Melitaea cinxia *Glanville Fritillary*

In Britain this fritillary occurs only on the southern coast of the Isle of Wight, on rough, uneven and stony dry ground in the 'undercliff'. Because it is so local it should be collected very sparingly. The Glanville Fritillary has a row of submarginal spots on the underside of the hind-wings, a feature which it shares only with Marsh Fritillary. However, the two species do not fly together. It is impossible to confuse the markings of the underside of the hind-wings with those of any other butterfly. There is a single generation in June. The caterpillar feeds mainly on ribwort plantain (*Plantago lanceolata*) but will eat other plantains.

I. lathonia

M. cinxia

H. semele

♂

♀

♀

H. semele
♀ u

Lasiommata
megera u
(see p. 64)

Lasiommata maera u
(see p. 64)

H. lycaon

♀ ♂

Hyponephele lycaon   *Dusky Meadow Brown*

This species, absent from the British Isles, is a survivor from warmer times in southern Finland and the Baltic, where it is rare. It occurs on arid sandy grassland, especially in clearings in woods and in bushy country. It resembles the Meadow Brown particularly in the underside markings. The stripe of scent-scales in the male is interrupted by the lighter-coloured veins. There is a single generation in July and August. The caterpillars feed on grasses, especially species of *Poa.*

Hipparchia semele   *Grayling*

The Grayling is a characteristic coastal species which flies commonly on arid sandy grasslands and heaths but it is also found inland on stony and hilly ground. The butterfly has an easily recognised quick and jerky zig-zag flight close to the ground, but does not often fly for great distances. It would rather rest with wings closed on the ground, on a stone or on a fallen treetrunk. When it comes to rest, the undersides of the fore-wings are raised to reveal the eye-marking (see illustration on p. 72); a moment later the fore-wings are lowered between the hind-wings and the eye disappears (see illustration on p. 66). Then, because the wings are angled to reduce the size of the shadow cast on the background, it becomes almost impossible to detect. The Grayling varies considerably in colour and there is a remarkable small dark race ssp. *thyone,* which occurs in northern Wales. This subspecies begins to emerge and fly at the end of June. Elsewhere the Grayling does not emerge until July and August, and occasionally in September. There is a single generation. The caterpillar lives on various grasses, particularly species of *Festuca* and *Deschampsia.*

H. semele

H. lycaon

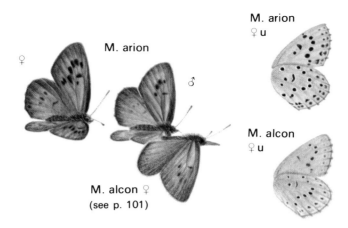

M. arion
♀ u

M. arion

♀

M. arion

♂

M. alcon
♀ u

M. alcon ♀
(see p. 101)

Maculinea arion   *Large Blue*

Large Blue has declined drastically over the last thirty years and is now extremely rare, if not extinct, in Britain. It is a protected species and must not be collected or disturbed. It is local in southern Scandinavia. It is essential that its habitat of dry open grassland or heathland be managed by grazing or burning because the ants, on which the caterpillar lives, cannot survive in tall vegetation (see p. 101). The butterfly has a single generation which flies from the end of June to August. The caterpillar initially feeds on wild thyme (*Thymus* spp.) and then as a parasite of ants.

Philotes baton   *Baton Blue*

Although there are two subspecies of Baton Blue in Europe, neither occurs in the British Isles. SSp. *baton* flies in central and western Europe and ssp. *schiffermuelleri* in Eastern Europe. They differ mainly in the structure of the male genitalia. The butterfly is found in southern Finland and the Baltic on dry slopes and sandy ground, with a single generation in June to mid-July. The caterpillar's diet is wild thyme (*Thymus* spp.). The Chequered Blue (p. 62), which also flies in southern Finland, is similar but larger and more heavily spotted on the underside.

P. baton

♂ u

♂

♀

P. dorylas

Plebicula dorylas *Turquoise Blue*

The Turquoise Blue, absent from the British Isles, is found in parts of southern Sweden and in the southern Baltic, flying over sunny grassland on dry chalky and sandy ground. It is easily distinguished from other species of Blue in the field because its underside looks almost white and it has unusually broad, chalky-white wing-fringes. Newly-emerged males, however, are such an intensely lustrous silver blue that no artist, or even a colour printing process, could reproduce it. The colour is a structural one, resulting from light refraction from the microscopic ridges on the scales of the wings. The butterfly has a single generation in July and August, although there are two broads in southern Europe. Melilots (*Melilotus* spp.) and kidney vetch (*Anthyllis vuneraria*) are the foodplants of the caterpillars.

Copper
(see pp. 96–7)

Copper
(see pp. 96–7)

M. arion

P. baton

P. dorylas

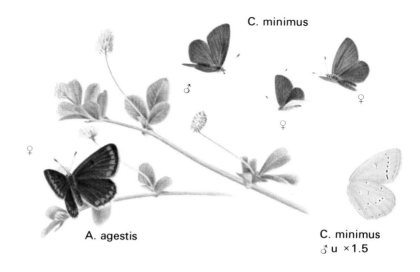

C. minimus

♂

♀

♀

♀

A. agestis

C. minimus
♂ u ×1.5

Aricia agestis *Brown Argus*

Lepidopterists now consider the Brown Argus and Northern Brown Argus (p.105) as different species. It is sometimes difficult to distinguish between them by their outward appearance, although in the British Isles the Brown Argus always lacks the white discoidal upperside spot on the fore-wing and usually has larger orange 'lunules'. The two species may also be identified from their distribution, number of generations and host plants. The Brown Argus likes to fly over drier places than the northern species, frequently on chalky or sandy gound. There are two generations, the first in May and June and the second in July to the beginning of September; the Northern Brown Argus has a single generation in July and August. The limits of distribution are uncertain because it was only in the 1960s that the existence of two species was established. The caterpillar feeds on storksbill (*Erodium cicutarium*) and rock-rose (*Helianthemum chamaecistus*), usually attended by ants. The distribution map is on p. 105.

Cupido minimus *Small Blue*

One of northern Europe's smallest butterflies, this little Blue is local, thought often plentiful where it occurs, on dry, often sandy or chalky ground. It occurs sporadically throughout the British Isles to Caithness, but is commoner in the south. The butterfly has a weak fluttering flight, with the pale-coloured underside displayed as the wings beat so that it appears alternately dark and light. The wings of the male are powdered with lustrous silver blue scales which are often restricted to the base of the wings, but never totally absent. The small Blue flies as a single generation from late May to early July, or later; emergence seems to be prolonged in many localities. The eggs are laid on the florets of kidney vetch (*Anthyllis vulneraria*) and are very conspicuous; the caterpillar feeds in the flower-heads.

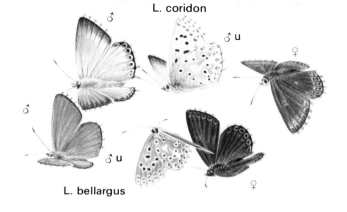

L. coridon

♂

♂ u

♀

♂

♂ u

L. bellargus

♀

Lysandra coridon   *Chalk-Hill Blue*

This attractive Blue is quite common on chalk downs and limestone grasslands in southern England. The conspicuous male appears silvery blue in flight but the brown females are difficult to spot. There is a single generation in July and August. Like the Adonis Blue, the caterpillars feed principally on horseshoe vetch (*Hippocrepis comosa*).

Lysandra bellargus   *Adonis Blue*

The male Adonis Blue is one of our most brilliantly-coloured species. It is found in southern England in the same type of country as Chalk-hill Blue, although it is more local and rare and seems to require much shorter vegetation. Populations of this species have declined more than most others, mainly because rabbits, which grazed the grassland short, have been greatly reduced in numbers by myxomatosis, a virus disease. Where both species fly together, supposed hybrids (f. *polonus*) are very occasionally found. The first generation flies in May and June and the second in August and September. The caterpillar feeds on horseshoe vetch (*Hippocrepis comosa*). Adonis and Chalk-Hill Blue females are very similar except that in the Adonis the pale colour of the spots on the hind-margin of the upperside of the hind-wings is blue, while in the Chalk-Hill Blue it is white.

C. minimus

L. coridon

L. bellargus

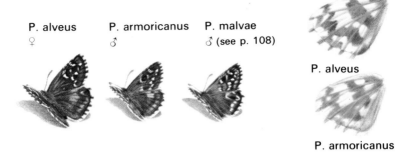

undersides of hind-wings ×2

P. alveus ♀ P. armoricanus ♂ P. malvae ♂ (see p. 108)

P. alveus

P. armoricanus

Pyrgus alveus *Large Grizzled Skipper*

This rare Skipper is a lowland species, except that in Norway it occurs at heights up to 1200 m. It is not found in the British Isles. Flight is over stony or sandy ground which has been warmed by the sun, particularly where there are scattered bushes to give shelter. Like other Skippers, it has a quick and whirling flight; it rests on the ground for a brief time and then shoots off like an arrow. Males are more extensively marked than females. Collectors may confuse this species with Oberthur's (see below). The caterpillar feeds on species of agrimony and cinquefoil (*Agrimonia* and *Potentilla* spp.).

Pyrgus armoricanus *Oberthür's Grizzled Skipper*

This Skipper flies rarely in Scandinavia over dry slopes warmed by the sun, and is not found at all in the British Isles. In northern Europe *P. armoricanus* is distinctly marked and is thus easily confused with *P. malvae* (Grizzled Skipper, p. 108). However, *P. malvae* flies as one generation only, while *P. armoricanus* has two. The first of these consists of small numbers of butterflies which occur in company with *P. malvae* in May, with the more numerous second generation flying in August to the beginning of September. Oberthur's Grizzled Skipper can also easily be confused with a small example of the Large species (see above), yet never occurs in the same place. *P. armoricanus* has a clearer dark spot in the discal area of the fore-wing and more distinct pale markings on the upper surfaces of the hind-wings. The caterpillar lives on species of wild strawberry and cinquefoil (*Fragaria* and *Potentilla* spp.).

P. alveus

P. armoricanus

Meadowland and marshes

Butterflies of damp grasslands and meadows, often near woods or parkland

A. cardamines

Anthocharis cardamines *Orange Tip*

Female Orange Tips are often confused with other Whites (see p. 117), but the male is unmistakable. When at rest on umbellifor flowers the bright orange of the fore-wings is covered by the cryptic pattern of the hind-wings, making the butterfly very inconspicuous. A single generation flies in meadows and along the edges of woods in May and June. Dwarf specimens, f. *minora*, occasionally occur (see p. 37). The caterpillar feeds mainly on the seed-pods of cuckoo-flower (*Cardamine pratensis*) and other Cruciferae.

Papilio machaon

The description of *Papilio machaon* is on p. 21.

Iphiclides podalirius *Scarce Swallowtail*

It is rare indeed to find a specimen of this elegant gliding butterfly in the British Isles, Denmark, Sweden or the Baltic. The species is a native of the Mediterranean countries, where it flies commonly but is rare in central Europe.

A. cardamines

I. podalirius

P. machaon
ssp. machaon ♀
(see p. 21)

I. podalirius
♀

81

♀ u

♀ f. valesina

♂

♀

A. paphia

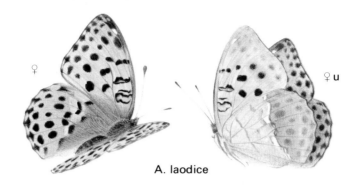

A. laodice

Argyronome laodice *Pallas's Fritillary*

Primarily a species of eastern Europe, Pallas's Fitillary flies over woodland meadows in the southern Baltic and occasionally elsewhere in Scandinavia. It does not occur in the British Isles. Like many other fritillaries, the female is paler than the male; the female illustrated has flown a great deal and is even paler than normal. Flight is slow compared with that of other fritillaries. There is a single generation in July and August. The caterpillar feeds on violets.

Argynnis paphia *Silver-washed Fritillary*

This, the largest of our fritillaries, flies quite commonly in woods with plenty of flowers. It frequently visits thistles and bramble-flowers, but is also seen among the treetops visiting a lime tree in blossom for example. A dark female form, f. *valesina*, occurs rarely with the type, but is commoner in some districts than others; the New Forest is one area where it is frequent. The Silver-Washed Fritillary is a powerful flier—it is on the wing in July and August as there is only one generation a year. The caterpillar usually feeds on violets (*Viola* spp.).

A. paphia

A. laodice

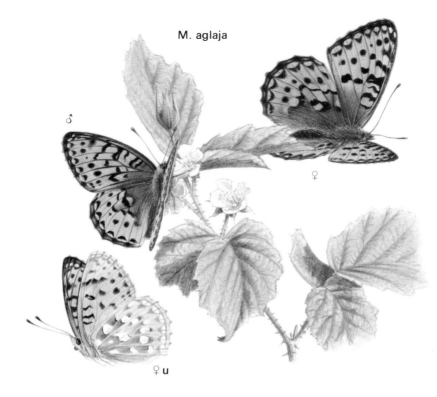

M. aglaja

♂

♀

♀ u

Mesoacidalia aglaja   *Dark Green Fritillary*

This species resembles other large fritillaries, but can be distinguished by the green markings of the underside of the wings. It flies quite commonly over meadows, downs and other grasslands and only infrequently in woodland. There is a single generation in late June and July. The butterfly is generally darker in the Hebrides (ssp. *scotica*) and northern Scotland. The caterpillar feeds on violets (*Viola* spp.).

M. aglaja

F. adippe

C. thore

♂

♀

F. adippe
(undersides of
the hind-wings are
illustrated on p. 69)

Fabriciana adippe   *High Brown Fritillary*

Generally less common than the Dark Green Fritillary, the High Brown prefers more wooded country. It also resembles the Niobe Fritillary, having two forms, with and without silver spots on the underside of the hind-wings. Both forms, f. *adippe* and f. *cleodoxa*, are illustrated with the Niobe Fritillary on p. 69. Specimens without silver spots are rather unusual in Britain and northern Europe. The male High Brown Fritillary has the veins of the fore-wings clearly thickened by scent-scales and is thus intermediate between the Niobe Fritillary with no thickening, and the Silver-washed Fritillary with pronounced thickening. There is a single generation in July and August. The caterpillar feeds on violets (*Viola spp.*).

Clossiana thore   *Thor's Fritillary*

There are two subspecies of Thor's Fritillary in Scandinavia, but neither occurs in the British Isles. Ssp. *carelia* is found in Karelia and ssp. *borealis* in northern Finland, Sweden and Norway, mainly in mountain birch woods. The upperside of the butterfly resembles that of Small Pearl-bordered Fritillary (p. 87), but the underside is characteristic. The caterpillar's diet is violets (*Viola* spp.).

C. thore
ssp. borealis
♀ u

undersides of hind-wings ×1.5

C. selene
ssp. hela

C. selene
ssp. selene

C. euphrosyne

Brenthis ino

C. titania
ssp. cypris

C. titania
ssp. cypris

♂

Clossiana titania   *Titania's Fritillary*

Absent from the British Isles, this butterfly flies over flowery damp meadowland and mosses in southern Finland and the Baltic as ssp. *rossica*, and in Sweden as the paler subspecies *cypris*. The upper surface is similar to that of several other fritillaries, but the species can easily be identified by the characteristic coloration and markings of the underside of the hind-wings. There is a single generation from the end of June to the beginning of August. The caterpillar lives on violets (*Viola* spp.) and knot-grasses (*Polygonum* spp.).

The markings on the upper wing surfaces vary far more than those of the hind-wings in all fritillary species. The patterning of the hind-wings is diagnostic for most species of fritillaries and this makes identification easy in most cases. Several examples of *C. selene* and *C. euphrosyne* are illustrated below to give some idea of the variation in upperside wing markings.

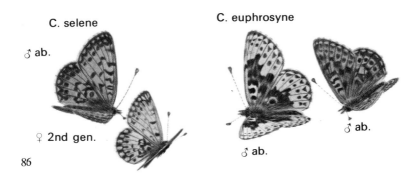

C. selene

♂ ab.

♀ 2nd gen.

C. euphrosyne

♂ ab.

♂ ab.

86

C. selene ♀   C. euphrosyne ♀

Clossiana selene   *Small Pearl-bordered Fritillary*

The two Pearl-bordered species are our most common smaller fritillaries. Their
upper surfaces are very similar but the Small Pearl-bordered Fritillary is not as
red. The main differences, however, are in the patterns on their undersides:
C. selene has distinct black angular markings and shinier mother-of-pearl-like
patches than *C. euphrosyne*. From central Scandinavia northwards there is a
smaller, darker form, ssp. *hela*, often with a pale underside and fewer mother-of-
pearl patches. The flying time is from June to the beginning of July in a single
generation, but in southern Scandinavia and very occasionally in England a
partial second generation flies in August in good years; these specimens are
smaller and not as heavily marked. Flight is over marshy flowery meadowland
and wooded country. The caterpillar feeds on various violets (*Viola* spp.).

Clossiana euphrosyne   *Pearl-bordered Fritillary*

This species is common in both marshy and dry grasslands, especially in woods.
Together with the Small Pearl-bordered Fritillary, it has disappeared in recent
years from many former sites in eastern England. Both are fast flyers, close to the
ground. The distinguishing features are described under *C. selene* and illustrated
on the preceding page. Like *C. selene*, there is a good deal of variation within
the species and melanistic forms are not difficult to find. The butterfly flies earlier
in the year than Small Pearl-bordered Fritillary, with a single generation in May
and June. The caterpillar feeds on violets (*Viola* spp.).

C. titania

C. selene

C. euphrosyne

M. athalia

Mellicta athalia *Heath Fritillary*

Although Heath Fritillary is common throughout most of Europe, it is a rarity in Britain and restricted to two small areas of distribution, one in Kent and one in Devon and Cornwall. It has disappeared from a few other sites in recent years. Two subspecies fly in northern Europe, ssp. *athalia* and ssp. *norvegica*, the latter mainly in the Fenno-Scandian mountain chain. The three butterflies illustrated are from the same area and show how varied the wing markings can be. Dark specimens may look very much like Assman's Fritillary (see p. 89): on the underside of the hind-wing the outermost narrow stripe and adjacent scalloped area have the same or almost the same light coloration in *M. athalia* while in *M. britomartis* the outer stripe is much darker. Another point of difference, the absence in the Heath Fritillary of a dark line at the hind-margin of this wing, as shown in the illustration on p. 89. *M. athalia* flies mainly in open woodland from June to the beginning of July. On rare occasions there is a partial second generation in August. The caterpillar feeds on ribwort plantain (*Plantago lanceolate*) and the common cow-wheat (*Malampyrum pratense*). Woodland management appears to be important to the survival of Heath Fritillary. In overgrown woods the food plants tend to be shaded out, but coppicing encourages them.

M. athalia ssp. norvegica

♂

| M. athalia | M. britomartis | Melitaea diamina |

underside of hind-wings ×1.5

M. britomartis
♀

Mellicta britomartis   *Assmann's Fritillary*

Because of its close similarity to the Heath Fritillary *M. britomartis* was long regarded as a variant. The illustrations show the main differences between these two species. As *M. britomartis* was only recently recognised as a species in its own right, its distribution is not yet fully known; it is not found in the British Isles. The butterfly flies in a single generation over the same kind of ground as the Heath Fritillary but somewhat later, at the end of June and July. Where the two species fly together *M. britomartis* is seen to be obviously darker. The sexes are similarly marked. The larva lives on plantains and speedwells (*Plantago* and *Veronica* spp.).

 *M. athalia*

M. britomartis

M. diamina
(the underside of hind-wing
is illustrated on p. 89)

Melitaea diamina   *False Heath Fritillary*

This rare fritillary occurs locally in damp woodland meadows, most often in the southernmost parts of Sweden; it is not found in the British Isles. It is easily confused with *M. athalia* and *M. britomartis*; the undersides of the hind-wings of all three species are illustrated on p. 89. *M. diamina* is more like *M. britomartis* —the undersides of their hind-wings have the light-coloured spots in a field divided by a dark line. The dark spots in the outmost brown submarginal stripe on the underside of the hing-wings of *M. diamina* are its most reliable distinguishing feature. Like other species of the *Melitaea* group, its flight is rather weak and close to the ground. There is a single generation in June. The caterpillar usually feeds on common cow-wheat (*Melampyrum pratense*).

M. diamina

E. aurinia

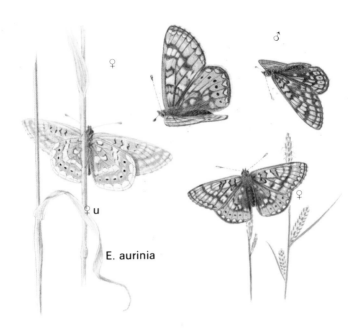

E. aurinia

Euphydyas aurinia   *Marsh Fritillary*

Two identical specimens are sometimes difficult to find because the variations within the species are so considerable. It appears sporadically and locally over both dry and damp grasslands—abundantly in some years and almost never in others. There are probably relatively few permanent colonies from which many 'overflow' populations appear in good years. The Marsh Fritillary occurs mainly in the west of England and Scotland but has disappeared from many areas in eastern England; it can also be found in Ireland. In the field the butterfly flies so low and fast it is hard to follow. Its habit of sitting on grass-stems with wings outspread gives the observer a better opportunity to examine it, but one can rarely approach close enough to see the markings distinctly.

The distribution map does not reflect the real chance of finding Marsh Fritillary; although it can occur over wide areas, it is extremely local within them. Because it lives in colonies there can be a large population in an area of less than an acre, but then it may be totally absent for miles around. The caterpillars, which over-winter colonially in a 'nest' spun from silk, are fairly conspicuous in spring. When they mature, the individuals from a nest separate and are more difficult to find. There is a single generation each year that flies mainly in June. The larva usually lives on Devil's-bit scabious (*Succisa pratensis*).

M. galathea ♀

A. hyperantus

♂ u

♀

Melanargia galathea   *Marbled White*

This unmistakably marked butterfly can hardly be confused with any other British species, except perhaps at a distance, when it could be mistaken for one of the Whites. It occurs throughout southern England, ranging as far north as the Yorkshire Wolds but is scarce or absent from East Anglia. It is found on most kinds of dry grasslands, including woodland clearings and edges and is often plentiful on chalk and limestone soils. The male is somewhat smaller and whiter than the female. The single generation is on the wing mainly in July. The caterpillar feeds on various grasses. The female scatters her eggs at random over the vegetation instead of attaching them individually to the foodplant.

Aphantopus hyperantus   *Ringlet*

The Ringlet is a common butterfly in southern England but becomes rarer further north and in Scotland. Occasionally the eye-spots on the underside are greatly elongated, reduced to white points or are missing altogether. The newly emerged specimens can look almost black, particularly the male. When it has been flying for some days, however, the upperside is uniform dull brown. The Ringlet occurs mainly in wooded country, or where there is well-developed scrub and often rests on brambles. It is on the wing as a single generation from the end of June until the middle of August. Like most satyrid larvae, the caterpillar feeds on grasses.

M. galathea

A. hyperantus

M. jurtina

ssp. jurtina

ssp. splendida

M. jurtina

Maniola jurtina   *Meadow Brown*

This is the commonest British butterfly thoughout the British Isles, except in the Shetlands. It is usually abundant in every kind of grassy place: downs, fields, meadows, the edges of wood and roadside verges. The flight is from the middle of June to September. There are two generations or, more probably, a single extended period of emergence. The female is larger and more brightly coloured, with more orange, than the male. The two sexes were originally described as separate species! Various grasses are the foodplants of the caterpillars.

The subspecies *Maniola jurtina splendida* differs from the usual form mainly in its more extensive yellow-orange colouring. It flies in northern Scotland, the Hebrides and Orkneys as well as in Ireland, the Isle of Man and the Scilly Isles.

Lasiommata
maera ♀
(see p. 64)

93

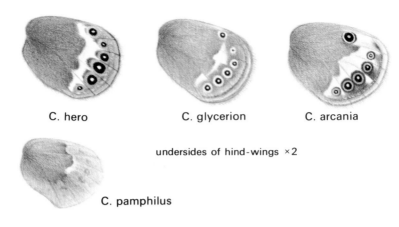

C. hero   C. glycerion   C. arcania

undersides of hind-wings ×2

C. pamphilus

Coenonympha pamphilus *Small Heath*

This is another very common satyrid which is numerous on most grassland but seldom visits flowers. During the usually slow and fluttering flight the hind-wings are occasionally held still and only the fore-wings move; this peculiar flight characteristic can also be observed in several other Satyridae. The ground colour of the Small Heath, normally pale yellow ochre, can vary from darkest brown to almost white. It flies from May to September, and is usually stated to have two generations in the south. Recent work suggests, however, that the annual cycle may be more complex. The caterpillar feeds on various grasses. The Small Heath can be confused with the Large Heath (p. 29) particularly the pale subspecies *scotica*.

Coenonympha glycerion *Chestnut Heath*

This is a central European species which, in the east of its range, reaches Finland where it may be locally common in wooded country and in damp meadows. It cannot be found in the British Isles. The upper surface of the female is paler than the male and more closely resembles a Small Heath. The Chestnut Heath flies in a single generation in June and July. The caterpillar eats grasses. Where they fly together the Chestnut Heath may be confused with either the Small or Large Heaths.

C. glycerion
♂

C. glycerion

C. pamphilus

C. arcania ♂

C. hero ♀

Coenonympha arcania *Pearly Heath*

Pearly Heath is mainly a coastal species in northern Europe and flies in bushy country and at the edges of deciduous woods. It is absent from the British Isles and occurs sparsely within the greater part of its range; it is common only in eastern central Sweden. All the eye-spots may be missing from the upper surface. There is a single generation which flies in June and July. The larva lives on grasses, like other Heaths.

Coenonympha hero *Scarce Heath*

Unlike the Pearly Heath, this is mainly an inland species; it does not occur in the British Isles. It flies in open woodland and over two entirely different biotopes: small water-meadows and dry grassland, often where there is newly planted spruce or fir. The butterfly is rare and very local, but is sometimes common in one particular small area. Its flight differs from related species; it often rises as high as one or two metres above the ground. The Scarce Heath flies in May and June in a single generation. The male is similar to the female but rather darker, lacks the eye-spots on the fore-wings and has less distinct markings on the hind-wings. The caterpillar lives on grasses.

C. pamphilus

C. arcania

C. hero

H. virgaureae

Heodes virgaureae   *Scarce Copper*

The Scarce Copper is one of those species recorded as British in the early nineteenth century but either an error was made or the species rapidly became extinct; it certainly does not occur in the British Isles now. The underside markings distinguish the female from other Copper butterflies. The Scarce Copper flies in July and August, with a single generation each year. It is found mainly in damp places where there are plenty of flowers. Ssp. *oranulus*, with smaller and paler females, flies in northern Scandinavia. The larval foodplants are sorrels and docks (*Rumex* ssp.).

H. virgaureae

L. phlaeas

H. tityrus

♂ 2nd gen. ♂ 1st gen.

L. phlaeas

Lycaena phlaeas *Small Copper*

One of our more common butterflies this quick and lively Copper can be seen at almost any time during the summer on flowery roadside verges, meadows and on dry grasslands. It is a particularly sun-loving species. There may be a third generation in October in the British Isles, but elsewhere there are usually two. The first, which is quite small and more weakly marked than the summer generation, flies in May and June. The second summer generation is large, vividly marked and has a more distinct tail on the hind-wing. The sexes have similar markings. Ssp. *polaris*, essentially a mountain form, occurs in northern Scandinavia. The upper surface of the hind-wings quite often has a row of small blue spots in front of the orange-coloured marginal band. The caterpillar lives on sorrels and docks (*Rumex* spp.), particularly sheep's sorrel (*R. acetosella*), but occasionally also on knot-grass (*Polygonum* spp.).

Heodes tityrus *Sooty Copper*

Absent from Britain, this species was found at one time on the Danish islands, but has now almost entirely disappeared. Its habitat is rather dry flowery ground at the edges of woods. There are two generations, in May and in July and August. The caterpillar feeds on docks (*Rumex* ssp.).

H. tityrus

♂

♀ u

♀

Lycaena helle ♂
(see p. 30)

97

♂ ssp. euridice

♂ ssp. stiberi

♀
ssp. stiberi

♀
ssp. hippothoe

♀ u
ssp. euridice

♀ u ssp. stiberi

♀
ssp. euridice

P. hippothoe

Palaeochrysophanus hippothoe   *Purple-edged Copper*

One of the less common Coppers, the Purple-edged occurs as three subspecies in
northern Europe but not in the British Isles. Ssp. *stiberi* is the most northerly,
distributed over almost all of Norway, parts of Sweden and northern Finland.
Further south it becomes ssp. *hippothoe* which flies alongside ssp. *euridice* in
extensive areas of south-eastern Norway and central Sweden. The northern ssp.
stiberi flies over meadowland but the southern subspecies prefers damper
grasslands and mosses. In the south the dark powdering is more extensive on the
upper surface of the fore-wings of the female and the marginal bands of the upper
surface of the hind-wings become narrower; they are entirely absent in the male.
When flying in the sunshine the male may appear a lustrous purple shade from
certain angles. Purple-edged Copper flies for a single generation in June and July,
and is usually very local. The caterpillar lives on docks and sorrels (*Rumex* spp.)
and on knot-grass (*Polygonum* spp.).

♀ ♂

L. dispar ssp. rutila

Lycaena dispar   *Large Copper*

The large and resplendent ssp. *dispar* formerly occurred in England but has been extinct since the middle of the nineteenth century. It was very similar to ssp. *batava* from northern Holland which was reintroduced in 1926 into Woodwalton Fen near Huntingdon in what is now Cambridgeshire. Ssp. *rutila*, illustrated above, was distributed over large areas of Europe at one time but now occurs only very locally. The species is known, however, to disappear from a particular locality for several years, and then reappear quite suddenly. An important factor that has contributed to the decline of Large Copper is its dependence on marshy ground with rich vegetation. Many of these areas have now been drained and put under cultivation; drainage affects an entire area and few fens or marshes survive. The Large Copper resembles both the Scarce and the Purple-edged Copper. The underside has similar markings to those of the latter but the ground colour of the hind-wings is light blue-grey. Ssp *rutila* flies for two generations, in June and July and from the end of August to September. Ssp *batava* is single-brooded, as was ssp. *dispar*, the old English form. The caterpillar, which must often survive prolonged immersion in flood-water during the winter, feeds on great water dock (*Rumex hydrolaphathum*). The pupa is often very conspicuous when attached to the upperside of a dock plant leaf, which makes it a target for predators.

P. hippothoe

L. dispar

♂ u

♂

E. argiades

Celastrina
argiolus ♂ u
(see p. 59)

Everes argiades   *Short-tailed Blue*

Short-tailed Blue has been taken very rarely in England, but occurs occasionally
in southern Finland and on Gotland in Sweden, where it may be resident. It flies
there in rather dry areas but prefers flowery and rather damp ground in central
Europe. As its name suggests, there is a small 'tail' projecting from the
hind-wings. The best identifying feature is its pale underside, rather like that of
Holly Blue, but with finer markings and two orange spots at the base of the tail.
The upper surface of the female is brown with a more or less widespread blue
lustre and frequently a few orange spots on the hind-wings near the tail. There
are two generations a year, in May and June and in July and August; the
individuals of the second brood are those usually seen in northern Europe. The
caterpillar feeds on bird's-foot trefoil (*Lotus corniculatus*), lucerne (*Medicago
sativa*) and clovers (*Trifolium* ssp.).

Lampides boeticus   *Long-tailed Blue*

Actually a resident of southern Europe and North Africa, this butterfly is a
notorious traveller—it reaches central Europe in late summer and very
occasionally extends as far as England.

It can be found in almost every subtropical country. In southern Europe the
Long-tailed Blue is continuously brooded throughout the summer and occurs as
several generations. A fast flyer, it may be difficult to spot. The female is dark brown
on the upper surface with lustrous violet-blue wing bases, while the male is a lustrous
purple-blue with dark wing margins. The underside is very distinctive for a butterfly
of northern Europe. The larva lives on a variety of leguminous plants, preferring
to feed on the unripe seed-pods.

L. boeticus
♂ u

♂   ♀

M. alcon ssp. alcon

Maculinea alcon *Alcon Blue*

The two subspecies of Alcon Blue differ in appearance and habit; ssp. *alcon* flies over mosses and water-meadows, while ssp *rebeli* prefers dry sandy slopes. Ssp *rebeli* has a greyer underside with fewer eye-spots than ssp. *alcon*, and the blue tone of its upper surface is purer and lighter, without the purple tinge. The female *M. alcon* can be very similar to the Large Blue (see p. 74). The Alcon Blue, rare in northern Europe and absent from the British Isles, is found in only a few areas in Sweden and Denmark, while ssp. *rebeli* has been identified from only a few places in northern Jutland. The species flies for a single generation in July and August. The caterpillars feed initially on species of gentian; those of ssp. *alcon* on marsh gentian (*Gentiana pneumonanthe*), and ssp. *rebeli* on various gentians of dryer biotopes. Later, they both feed on ant grubs.

There is a remarkable symbiotic relationship between the larvae of the Alcon Blue and the Large Blue and certain ant species. The butterfly larva lives on its host plant for the first few weeks of its life but then falls off and adopts a characteristic 'humped' attitude that makes it resemble an ant grub. The sugary secretion from a gland at the rear end of a caterpillar is very attractive to an ant, who 'milks' it and then carries the caterpillar down into its nest to feed on ant larvae. The caterpillar over-winters, continues to eat ant grubs, and finally pupates in the nest without, apparently, being in danger at any time. After three weeks in the pupa stage the butterfly emerges and, with wings still unexpanded, creeps along the passages in the nest and into the open air, where it climbs up a grass stem to stretch out and dry its wings. The Alcon Blue lives mainly in nests of the ant *Myrmica laevinodis* and the Large Blue in nests of *Myrmica sabuleti* and *M. scabrinodis*. The larvae of most blues (Lycaenidae) produce a secretion which attracts ants but the relationship with ants of our other European species is not as complex as those of the Alcon Blue and Large Blue, except perhaps in the case of the Idas Blue (p. 103). However, many other 'Blue' caterpillars are protected from ants in return for the secretion they produce.

L. boeticus

E. argiades

M. alcon

L. argyrognomon

Lycaeides argyrognomon   *Reverdin's Blue*

This species, absent from the British Isles, is rare in warm sunny parts of southern Scandinavia on dry slopes where milkvetch grows. The butterfly is very similar to the Idas Blue, but is easily distinguished from it in northern Europe by its large size and strikingly pale underside. There is a single generation in July and August. The caterpillar feeds on milkvetch (*Astragulus glycyphyllus*).

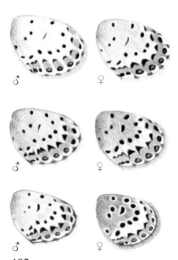

L. argyrognomon
Both sexes have lighter coloured undersides than argus and idas. The black, angular spots in front of the orange band are more rounded than in idas. The wing fringes of both sexes are white.

Idas Blue
The black angular spots in front of the orange band are sharply pointed in both sexes. The male's ground colour is slightly tinged with brown, which is stronger in the female. She also has brown shading on the wing fringes.

Silver-studded Blue
The male is not as brown-tinged as the Idas Blue. The ground colour of the female is strongly tinged with brown and the white rings around the spots are more distinct than in *L. idas*. The wing fringes are shaded brown.

102

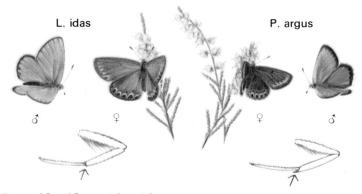

L. idas   P. argus

♂   ♀   ♀   ♂

Lycaeides idas   *Idas Blue*

The Idas Blue does not occur in the British Isles, but is common throughout Scandinavia, over all kinds of grassland. It varies considerably in size and markings, but is best identified by the features shown on the previous page and in the illustration above. In northern Scandinavia the species is rather smaller (ssp. *lapponicus*). The female often has extensive blue powdering, but this may be limited to the base of the wings. The flight, as a single generation, is from the end of June to August. The caterpillar feeds on various leguminous plants (Leguminosae), always in the vicinity of ants (*Lasius niger, Formica cinerea*, etc.), with which it lives symbiotically (cf. p. 101).

Plebejus argus   *Silver-studden Blue*

A local species, but often abundant where it occurs; in England it is predominantly a species of dry heathlands but may be also found on grasslands and, rarely, chalk downs. It is very similar to the Idas Blue (above), but is usually smaller. In northern Europe the males of both the Silver-studded and Idas Blue can always be distinguished by the tibia of the front legs, which in the Silver-studded Blue has a long spine at its tip. Local variation in form is common in this species. Several local races occur, or have occurred in Britain. One of the best known is a dwarf form which flies on the Great Orme's Head in northern Wales; it is on the wing about two weeks before the normal one. The usual flight period is July and August in a single brood. The caterpillars feed on a variety of plants, chiefly Leguminosae.

L. argyrognomon   *L. idas*   *P. argus*

A. artaxerxes
ssp. artaxerxes

♀

♂

A. nicias
ssp. scandica

♀

♂

A. artaxerxes
ssp. allous

♀

♂

E. eumedon

♀

undersides of female hind-wings ×2

A. artaxerxes
ssp. artaxerxes

A. artaxerxes
ssp. allous

A. nicias

E. eumedon

Aricia artaxerxes   *Mountain Argus*

Only recently accepted as a 'good' species, this butterfly occurs in Scotland and northern England and is distinguished primarily by its white discal spot. The male does not usually have orange spots on the fore-wings. There is a single generation from the end of June to the beginning of August. The host plant of the caterpillar is the common rock-rose (*Helianthemum chamaecistus*).

Aricia artaxerxes allous

This, the Scandinavian subspecies, flies over open but not marshy places. It is very similar to, and thus can be easily confused with, the Brown Argus (see p. 76), but does not usually have so many orange spots on the upper surface. The Mountain Argus can also be mistaken for those female Common Blues with little blue coloration (see p. 107). There is a single generation from the end of June to August. In common with other *Aricia* species, the Mountain Argus has a slow and rather weak flight near the ground. The larva lives on various cranesbills (*Geranium* spp.).

Aricia nicias   *Silvery Argus*

Usually rare in Scandinavia and not found in Britain, this butterfly occurs as a single generation in July and flies in warm sunny places, often over the same ground as the Geranium Argus (below). The Scandinavian form is ssp. *scandica*. The caterpillar, too, feeds on species of cranesbill (*Geranium* spp.).

Eumedonia eumedon   *Geranium Argus*

Another absentee from Britain, this rather rare species is found both on dry, sandy and on damp meadowland. Both ssp. *arenicola* and ssp. *praticola*, identified in southern Sweden, are rather larger than ssp. *borealis* which occurs in northern Scandinavia. There is a single generation which flies in June and July. The caterpillar also feeds on cranesbill (*Geranium* spp.).

A. agestis

A. artaxerxes

A. nicias

E. eumedon

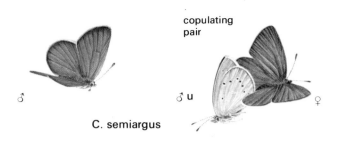

copulating pair

♂   ♂ u   ♀

C. semiargus

Cyaniris semiargus *Mazarine Blue*

This species flies rather commonly over meadowland in Scandinavia. There is little doubt that it was also resident in the British Isles until the mid-nineteenth century, but has now become extinct. Only a few chance sightings have been made in the twentieth century. As in other species of Blues, the greatest variation occurs on the undersides of the wings where some of the spots may be missing, extended into streaks or enlarged. Flight as a single generation is from the middle of June to July, and sometimes into August. The caterpillar feeds mainly on clovers (*Trifolium* spp.) but also on melilots (*Melilotus* spp.) and kidney vetch (*Anthyllis vulneraria*).

Plebicula amanda *Amanda's Blue*

This is a comparatively large species of Blue that does not occur in Britain but, although local, flies commonly in southern Scandinavia over woodland meadows, usually in small numbers. About half the females on the Scandinavian peninsula are extensively marked with blue, but this form is rare further south. Flight in a single generation is from June until August. The caterpillar feeds on tufted vetch (*Vicia cracca*).

P. amanda

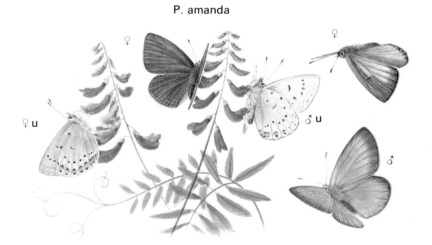

♀   ♀

♀ u   ♂ u   ♂

P. icarus

Polyommatus icarus *Common Blue*

The most numerous and familiar of our Blues, this species flies almost everywhere over open flowery ground. In Scotland, northern Ireland and norther Scandinavia there is a single generation in June and July. Elsewhere it can be seen throughout the summer from May until September; it flies as two overlapping generations. There is considerable variations, particularly on the underside where the spots may be smaller, enlarged or run together as streaks. The female's blue markings are more or less extensive, depending partly on climate. On warm days it congregates, like other Blues, to drink at patches of damp sand. In the evenings individuals often gather together in a particular spot to 'roost' or spend the night frequently on the flower-heads and stems of tall grasses. The larva lives on leguminous plants, especially bird's-foot trefoil (*Lotus corniculatus*)

P. amanda

C. semiargus

P. icarus

107

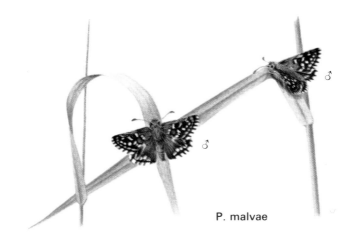

P. malvae

Pyrus malvae *Grizzled Skipper*

This species flies rather commonly over meadowland in Scandinavia. There is grassland at the edges of woods, in glades and in dry meadows and fields. The butterfly often sits on the ground, a leaf or a grass-stem, with wings spread out or half-closed in typical Skipper fashion. The species is normally single-brooded and flies in May and early June; there are records of individuals of a second generation in August in England but these are rare. The sexes are similarly marked but the male may always be recognised by a fold in the leading edge of the fore-wing which contains the scent-scales. The caterpillar feeds particularly on wild strawberry (*Fragaria vesca*) but also on cinquefoils and mallows (*Potentilla* and *Malva* spp.). Although only one *Pyrgus* species occurs in Britain, there are several in Europe and three in Scandinavia (see pp. 32 and 78).

The inexperienced observer can easily confuse the Grizzled Skipper with two species of geometrid moth which fly at the same time and also often sit with outspread wings. However, the behaviour of these moths in flight, and particularly in settling, is very different from that of the Grizzled Skipper and other butterflies. Anyone starting to collect butterflies will meet numbers of day-flying moths, but the behaviour of the different species will soon become familiar and the differences from butterflies more obvious.

P. malvae

C. palaemon

H. morpheus

C. palaemon
♀

C. silvicolus
♀
(see p. 60)

Carterocephalus palaemon *Chequered Skipper*

A very local species, it is rare in northern Europe, but more common in central Europe. Its flight is over flowery ground, in open woodland or along rides and at the edges of woods. The Chequered Skipper occurred in the Midlands of England (Lincolnshire, Northamptonshire, Cambridgeshire) but has not been seen for several years and may well have become extinct. However, it is well established in mid-western Scotland, where it flies at the edges of birch forests. There is some evidence that these Scottish localities are more like those of its central European habitats than the former localities in England. The sexes have similar markings, but the yellow spots are lighter in the female. The species resembles the Northern Chequered Skipper (p. 60), but can be distinguished by the upper surface of the hind-wings where the Chequered Skipper has fewer yellow spots than the northern species. There is a single generation in the latter half of May and June. The larva feeds on species of grasses but there is some controversy as to which ones they are.

Heteropterus morpheus *Large Chequered Skipper*

This species is not found in the British Isles, although it occurs in the Channel Islands and occasionally in southern Scandinavia. It flies in meadows with a characteristic bobbing flight close to the ground. The upper surfaces of the wings of both sexes are dark brown with a few obscure yellow markings near the fore-wing margins. There is a single brood which flies from the end of June to the beginning of August. The caterpillar lives on various grasses.

H. morpheus
♂ u

T. acteon

T. sylvestris

T. lineola

Illustrations ×1.5

In addition to the small differences in wing markings illustrated above, the tip of the antennal club helps to distinguish these three species, which are often confused. The underside of the tip of the antenna is reddish brown in the Small Skipper, but in the Essex Skipper it is usually black. All three species fly together in southern England, but the Lulworth Skipper is local and almost confined to the Dorset Coast. The Small and Essex Skippers fly together in parts of Denmark but only the Essex in the rest of Scandinavia.

Thymelicus acteon   *Lulworth Skipper*

Although restricted to coarse coastal grassland in Devon and particularly Dorset in southern England, this species is often very plentiful where it occurs. It has probably benefited from the spread of coarse grasses, especially tor-grass (*Brachypodium pinnatum*), following myxomatosis. The single generation flies in July and August. The caterpillar's diet is grasses, probably tor-grass in particular.

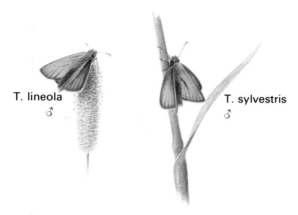

T. lineola ♂

T. sylvestris ♂

Thymelicus lineola   *Essex Skipper*

The Essex Skipper flies over grassland at the edges of woods, along woodland rides and among tall grasses on downs and hills. It visits many different kinds of flowers, particularly scabious and thistles. Common in eastern England as far north as Lincolnshire, it is much more local in the western part of southern England. Unlike the Small Skipper, it is not known to occur in Wales. Like other Skippers, it sits in the sun, with fore-wings held half-closed and hind-wings spread out flat. The differences between the Essex Skipper and the very similar Small Skipper are shown on the facing page. The Essex Skipper has a single generation in July and August. The caterpillar eats various types of grasses.

Thymelicus sylvestris   *Small Skipper*

Although found in the same habitat as Essex Skipper, the distribution of the Small Skipper is much wider. It is common from Yorkshire and Northern Wales southwards, and throughout south-western England. There is a single generation in July and August. Like its relatives, the caterpillar feeds on various grass species and spins a silken tube or retreat in which it lives when not actually feeding.

T. acteon

T. lineola

T. sylvestris

111

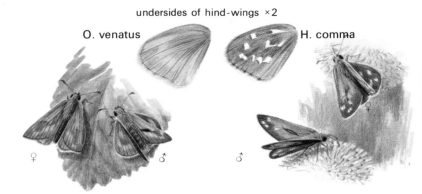

undersides of hind-wings ×2

O. venatus

H. comma

♀

♂

♂

Hesperia comma *Silver-spotted Skipper*

Very local in Britain, this species is confined to chalk and limestone hills in Southern England and is rare in Scandinavia. It resembles the Large Skipper (below), but can be easily distinguished from it by the white spots on the underside of the hind-wings. Also, the spots on the upperside are more definite and there are other minor differences. The butterfly prefers short open grassland and has disappeared from many former haunts in England, probably as a result of the growth of coarse grasses following the myxomatosis epidemic. The flight is low and quick and the butterfly frequently settles on the ground. It is later on the wing than the Large Skipper, flying in late July and August as a single generation. The caterpillar lives on grasses, probably mainly on sheep's fescue (*Festuca ovina*).

Ochlodes venatus *Large Skipper*

Common on tall grassland, and often at the edges of woods or scrub, the behaviour of this butterfly is restless; it sits for a moment on a leaf with wings in the characteristic Skipper position, and then darts away to settle again for a few seconds. Like all butterflies, it is more active in hot sunny weather. The Large Skipper, a frequent visitor to flowers, is able to take nectar from a large number of different blooms with its long tongue. There is a single generation from mid-June to the beginning of August. Various grasses are the larval foodplants.

H. comma

O. venatus

Cultivated land

Butterflies whose habitat is
farmland, roadside verges, gardens,
urban parks and fields with clover
and lucerne

Pieris brassicae *Large White*

The Large White, Green-veined White and Small White are commonly known under the generic term Cabbage Whites. Most gardeners will recognise the caterpillars of these pests which feed so voraciously on cabbages and almost all other cultivated cruciferous plants. Despite various attempts at control measures, the Cabbage White caterpillars are difficult to keep in check. In small gardens where a close watch can be kept on the crop, the Large White is probably a less insidious pest than Small White because the eggs are laid in large groups. They, and the young caterpillars which hatch from them and live together while small, can be more easily located and destroyed. But if numbers of Large White caterpillars 'get away' they will strip a cabbage patch in a very few days. The caterpillars are evil-smelling and distasteful to birds; the yellow and black of the Large White larva, which contrasts so remarkably with those of the green camouflage of the Small White, is a good example of 'warning coloration'—an advertisement to any predator that the prospective prey is nauseous or actually dangerous. However, Large White caterpillars have many other enemies and, being gregarious, are particularly vulnerable to virus disease. Despite being a pest and thus under attack, the Large White survives and, although its numbers fluctuate, it is generally common throughout the British Isles and is the only butterfly to be widespread in the Shetlands. There are usually two generations a year, in May and June and July and August, but Large White is a strongly migratory species, and in Britain the resident spring population is reinforced each year, to a greater or lesser extent, by immigrants from the Continent. The spring brood is more lightly marked on the upperside, but darker on the underside, than the summer brood.

Pieris rapae *Small White*

This butterfly resembles the Large White, but is usually smaller; small examples of the latter are generally more darkly marked underneath and have more extensive black markings above. The Small White flies as two generations, at the same times and with the same differences in markings as the large White. It occurs throughout the British Isles but is less common in the north. Although either species may be the commoner at any one time, the Small White is usually the more abundant, especially in the summer generation. The solitary green caterpillars, which can be just as damaging to cabbages as Large White larvae, also feed on other cruciferous plants.

P. brassicae

P. rapae

P. brassicae
♂

P. rapae
♀

P. rapae
♂

P. rapae
♀ u

P. brassicae
♀ u

P. brassicae
♀

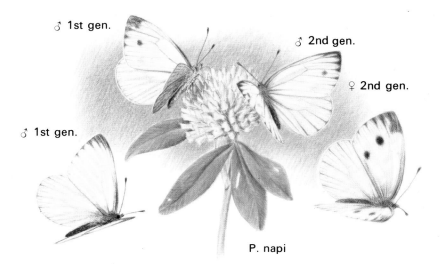

♂ 1st gen.

♂ 2nd gen.

♀ 2nd gen.

♂ 1st gen.

P. napi

Pieris napi   *Green-veined White*

This is another very common and abundant butterfly that sometimes flies in company with the Large and Small Whites over cultivated ground, but occurs much more frequently on grasslands, in fens and wet meadowland and along woodland rides. There are two generations of the Green-veined White, the first in May and June and the second from the end of July through to August. Butterflies of the first generation are not as heavily marked on the upper surface but the underside green veining is well marked. The second generation is more strongly marked on the upper surface but has less distinct, sometimes almost invisible, green veins on the underside. This species is one of the most variable of all butterflies, both in its ground colour which can range from pure white to bright yellow, and in the intensity and size of the dark markings of both upper and underside. Like the Large and Small Whites, the Green-veined White female has one more black spot than the male on the upperside of the fore-wing. The butterfly occurs throughout the British Isles except in the Shetlands. The caterpillar feeds on many different cruciferous plants but not as frequently on cabbages and other crops as the Large or Small Whites.

P. napi

P. napi
ssp. bicolorata
♀

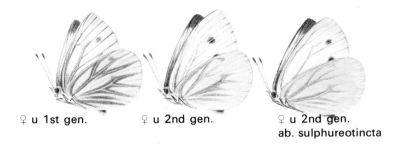

♀ u 1st gen.　　　　♀ u 2nd gen.　　　　♀ u 2nd gen.
　　　　　　　　　　　　　　　　　　　　　ab. sulphureotincta

Our white or pale yellow butterflies with dark tips to the fore-wings are illustrated below. The three species in the top row are fast fliers, but the others have a slower and more fluttering flight. The Clouded Yellows (top left and top right) are usually pale yellow with reddish fringes to the wings; the Moorland Clouded Yellow prefers bogs while the Pale Clouded Yellow likes fields of clover and lucerne. The two species (centre) most often fly in wooded country, the Wood White weakly and slowly. The markings of the female Orange Tip resemble the Cabbage Whites (below) but the butterflies are easily distinguished by the mottled green markings on the underside of the hind-wing.

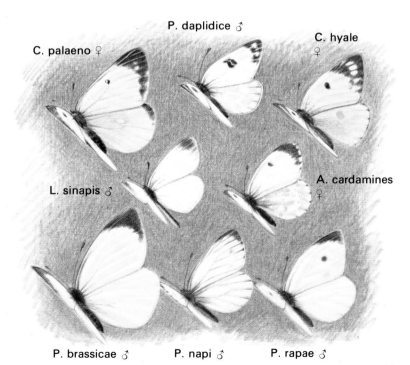

P. daplidice ♂

C. palaeno ♀

C. hyale ♀

L. sinapis ♂

A. cardamines ♀

P. brassicae ♂　　　　P. napi ♂　　　　P. rapae ♂

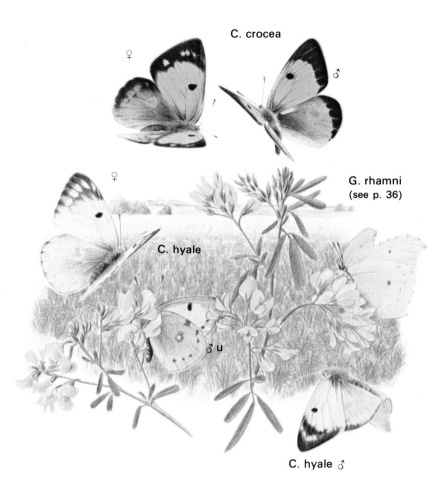

C. crocea

♀

♂

♀

G. rhamni
(see p. 36)

C. hyale

♂ u

C. hyale ♂

Colias crocea *Clouded Yellow*

In common with several other Clouded Yellow species this very migratory butterfly comes to northern Europe from the Mediterranean countries, where it flies commonly in favourable years. Some reach Britain nearly every year but the map is only the roughest guide to distribution. The Clouded Yellow has a rapid but usually level flight. It is found most frequently in late summer and early autumn, as the progeny of immigrants earlier in the year. It flies on downs and grasslands but particularly frequents fields of clover and lucerne. In southern Europe it is continuously brooded and has several generations during the summer. The caterpillar feeds on a variety of leguminous plants, especially lucerne (*Medicago sativa*) and vetches (*Vicia* spp.).

C. hyale ♂

The external differences between the Pale Clouded Yellow and Berger's Clouded Yellow are not consistent; the latter usually has a more rounded fore-wing, yellower ground colour and a brighter orange discal spot on the hind-wings. The marginal dark markings are weaker in Berger's Clouded Yellow as is the dark dusting at the base of the fore-wing; this dark dusting also extends further along the rear margin of the wing.

C. australis ♂

Colias hyale   *Pale Clouded Yellow*

Like the other Clouded Yellows described on these two pages, the Pale Clouded Yellow is only an occasional visitor to Britain. In Scandinavia, however, it is found every year. It, too, flies close to the ground and at great speed. The yellow tones of the male are rarely found in the female. There are two generations, in May and June and in August. Butterflies of the first generation are considerably scarcer than those of the second. The best chance of finding Pale Clouded Yellow is in clover and lucerne fields in late summer, where it often flies with Large Whites, Brimstones, Small Tortoiseshells and Peacocks.

Colias australis   *Berger's Clouded Yellow*

Encountered only very occasionally in northern Europe, this species is a native of the Mediterranean countries, where it usually flies over drier and more arid ground than the Pale Clouded Yellow. There are two or three generations, almost continuously from May until September. Although it is so similar to the Pale Clouded Yellow in the adult state, the caterpillars and foodplants are very different. The larva of Berger's Clouded Yellow is conspicuously spotted and feeds almost exclusively on horseshoe vetch (*Hippocrepis comosa*) and crown vetch (*Coronilla varia*).

C. crocea

C. hyale

C. australis

♀

♀ u

I. io

Inachis io *Peacock*

The Peacock, one of our best-known and most beautiful butterflies, flies in a single generation from the end of July until September, and in late summer often visits garden flowers such as buddleia in company with Red Admiral, Painted Lady, Brimstone and other species. After hibernation, which is often indoors, it flies again from March to May or later at the edges of woods and along woodland rides where it visits sallow catkins (see p. 45) or suns itself on patches of bare ground. The species has recently extended its range both in the British Isles and Scandinavia. In the last half of the nineteenth century and early in the twentieth it was hardly ever found in Scotland but its expansion of range, which began in the late 1930s, has now taken it into many parts of Scotland, although it is by no means general in the north. It occurs throughout England and Wales. The undersides of the wings are almost black when the butterfly is fresh and the pattern and coloration of the upperside are unmistakable. The black spiny caterpillars live gregariously on nettles (*Urtica dioica*).

I. io

V. cardui

V. atalanta

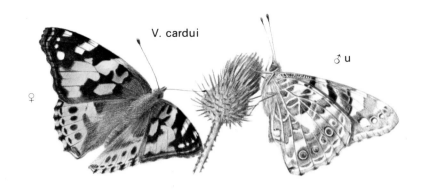

V. cardui

♀   ♂ u

Vanessa cardui   *Painted Lady*

The Painted Lady is the world's most widely distributed butterfly, absent only from the polar regions and South America where there are two similar species. It makes an annual migration northwards from North Africa and spreads over all Europe. Immigrating females of the spring generation lay their eggs in July in northern Europe to produce more butterflies in later summer but they cannot survive during the winter further north than central Europe. The butterfly is found in the British Isles every year, although it is rare in some and common in others. The caterpillar lives solitarily, usually on thistles (*Cirsium* and *Carduus* spp.) but is also known to feed on many other plants.

Vanessa atalanta   *Red Admiral*

The life cycle of the Red Admiral, also a migrant to Britain, is similar to that of Painted Lady. The butterflies visit gardens with rotting fruit in late summer and autumn, but are frequently also found at flowers, particularly buddleia and michaelmas daisies. Some fly south in the autumn to hibernate; there are a few authentic records of successful over-wintering in Britain. The Red Admiral is seen every year, but its numbers vary. The caterpillars live singly on nettles (*Urtica dioica*).

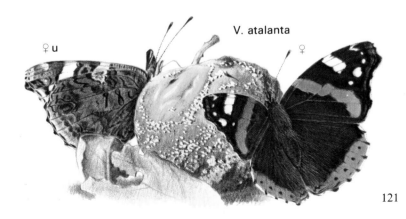

♀ u   V. atalanta   ♀

A. urticae

Aglais urticae *Small Tortoiseshell*

One of our best-known butterflies, it is common near cultivated ground, in gardens and, particularly after hibernation, at the edges of woods and along woodland rides (see p. 45). There are two generations each year in the British Isles, but only one in Scandinavia. Butterflies of the first brood fly from late June onwards and those of the second in August and September; these over-winter to appear in spring, when they pair and the females lay their eggs. This species usually hibernates indoors. Many people have found a comatose Small Tortoiseshell behind a picture or in a dark corner during the depths of winter, or have released one that was fluttering against a window in the first sunshine of spring. The Small Tortoiseshell is darker in northern Europe than elsewhere, and in northern Scandinavia a form *polaris* has been identified, which flies with the typical form except in the extreme north-east, where it predominates. The gregarious caterpillars, which feed on nettles (*Urtica dioica*), are easy to find and rear.

Further reading

There are numerous books on butterflies, both in and out of print, and the beginner should have little difficulty in acquiring a basic library. However, many of them do not go much beyond identification, classification, variation and simple accounts of life histories. Those that discuss ecology and behaviour are particularly desirable but not many have been published. Recommended are:

Carter, D.J. *The Observer's Book of Caterpillars* (Frederick Warne, London, 1979)

Dennis, R.L.H. *The British Butterflies: Their Origin and Establishment* (Classey, Faringdon, 1977)

Ford, E.B. *Butterflies*, 4th edn (Collins, London, 1977)

Higgins, L.G. and Riley N.D. *A Field Guide to the Butterflies of Britain and Europe*, 3rd edn (Collins, London, 1975)

Howarth, T.G. *South's British Butterflies* (Frederick Warne, London, 1973)

Smart, P. *The Illustrated Encyclopaedia of the Butterfly World in Colour* (Hamlyn, London, 1976)

Journals

Original papers and other articles on butterflies are widely dispersed in the literature. Two periodicals which contain many papers on butterflies are:

The Entomologist's Gazette

The Entomologist's Record and Journal of Variation

Societies

The Royal Entomological Society of London, 41 Queen's Gate, London SW7 5HU

The British Entomological and Natural History Society, c/o Alpine Club, 74 South Audley Street, London W1Y 5FF

The Amateur Entomologist's Society, enquiries (s.a.e.) to 18 Golf Close, Stanmore, Middlesex HA7 2PP

The British Butterfly Conservation Society, Tudor House, Quorn, Lough-borough, Leics, LE12 8AD

Equipment

Watkins & Doncaster, Four Throws, Hawkhurst, Kent

Worldwide Butterflies, Over Compton, Sherborne, Dorset

L. Christie, 129 Franciscan Road, Tooting, London SW17 8DZ (postal only)

A. urticae

Checklist of species and subspecies

Papilionidae
Papilio L.
  machaon L.
    ssp. *britannicus* Seitz
Iphiclides Hübner
  podalirius L.
Parnassius Latreille
  apollo L.
    ssp. *linnaei* Bryk
  mnemosyne L.
    ssp. *argiope* Früstorfer
    ssp. *romani* Bryk

Pieridae
Pieris Schrank
  brassicae L.
  rapae L.
  napi L.
Pontia F.
  daplidice L.
Aporia Hübner
  crataegi L.
Anthocharis Boisduval
  cardamines L.
Colias F.
  palaeno L.
    ssp. *europome* Esper
  crocea Geoffroy
  hyale L.
  australis Verity
Gonepteryx Leach
  rhamni L.
Leptidea Billberg
  sinapis L.

Nymphalidae
Apatura F.
  iris L.
Limenitis F.
  populi L.
  camilla L.
Nymphalis Kluk
  antiopa L.
  polychloros L.
  xanthomelas Schiffermüller
  vaualbum Schiffermüller
Inachis Hübner
  io L.
Vanessa F.
  atalanta L.
  cardui L.
Aglais Dalman
  urticae L.
Polygonia Hübner
  c-album L.
Araschnia Hübner
  levana L.
Argynnis F.
  paphia L.

Argyronome Hübner
  laodice Pallas
Mesoacidalia Reuss
  aglaja L.
    ssp. *scotica* Watkins
Fabriciana Reuss
  adippe Schiffermüller
  niobe L.
Issoria Hübner
  lathonia L.
Brenthis Hübner
  ino Rottemburg
Boloria Moore
  aquilonaris Stichel
    ssp. *alethea* Hemming
Proclossiana Reuss
  eunomia Esper
    ssp. *ossianus* Herbst
    ssp. *montana* Petersen
    ssp. *subargentata* Petersen
Clossiana Reuss
  selene Schiffermüller
    ssp. *hela* Staudinger
  euphrosyne L.
  titania Esper
    ssp. *cypris* Meigen
    ssp. *rossica* Hemming
  freija Thunberg
  thore Hübner
    ssp. *carelia* Valle
    ssp. *borealis* Staudinger
  frigga Thunberg
Melitaea F.
  cinxia L.
  diamina Lang
Mellicta Billberg
  athalia Rottemburg
    ssp. *norvegica* Aurivillius
  britomartis Assman
Euphydryas Scudder
  maturna L.
  aurinia Rottemberg

Satyridae
Melanargia Meigen
  galathea L.
Hipparchia F.
  semele L.
    ssp. *thyone* Thompson
  alcyone Schiffermüller
    ssp. *norvegica* Staudinger
Oeneis Hübner
  jutta Hübner
Erebia Dalman
  ligea L.
  euryale Esper
    ssp. *euryaloides* Tengström

epiphron Knoch
  aethiops Esper
  embla Thunberg
  disa Thunberg
Maniola Schrank
  jurtina L.
    ssp. *splendida* White
Hyponephele Muschamp
  lycaon Kuhns
Aphantopus Wallengren
  hyperantus L.
Pyronia Hübner
  tithonus L.
Coenonympha Hübner
  tullia Müller
    ssp. *demophile* Freyer
    ssp. *rothleibii* Herrich-Schäffer
    ssp. *scotica* Staudinger
  pamphilus L.
  arcania L.
  glycerion Borkhausen
  hero L.
Pararge Hübner
  aegeria L.
    ssp. *tircis* Butler
    ssp. *oblita* Harrison
Lasiommata Westwood
  megera L.
  maera L.
  petropolitana F.
Lopinga Moore
  achine Scopoli
    ssp. *suecia* Bryk
    ssp. *rambringi* Bryk

Nemeobiidae
Hamearis Hübner
  lucina L.

Lycaeidae
Thecla F.
  betulae L.
Quercusia Verity
  quercus L.
Nordmannia Tutt
  ilicis Esper
Strymonidia Tutt
  w-album Knoch
  pruni L.
Callophrys Billberg
  rubi L.
Lycaena F.
  helle Schiffermüller
  phlaeas L.
    ssp. *polaris* Courvoisier
  dispar Haworth
    ssp. *rutila* Werneberg
    ssp. *batava* Oberthür

124

Heodes Dalman
  virgaureae L.
    ssp. *oranula* Freyer
  tityrus Poda
Paraeochrysophanus Verity
  hippothoe L.
    ssp. *stiberi* Gerhard
    ssp. *euridice* Rottemburg
Lampides Hübner
  boeticus L.
Everes Hübner
  argiades Pallas
Cupido Schrank
  minimus Fuessly
Celastrina Tutt
  argiolus L.
Glaucopsyche Scudder
  alexis Poda
    ssp. *schneideri* Staudinger
Maculinea Van Eecke
  alcon Schiffermüller
    ssp. *rebeli* Hirschke
  arion L.
Philotes Scudder
  baton Bergsträsser
    ssp. *schiffermuelleri*
    Hemming

Scolitantides Hübner
  orion Pallas
Plebejus Kluk
  argus L.
Lycaeides Hübner
  idas L.
    ssp. *lapponicus* Gerhard
  argyrognomon Bergsträsser
Vacciniina Tutt
  optilete Knoch
    ssp. *cyparissus* Hübner
Eumedonia Forster
  eumedon Esper
    ssp. *borealis* Wahlgren
    ssp. *praticola* Burrau
    ssp. *arenicola* Burrau
Aricia Reichenbach
  agestis Schiffermüller
  artaxerxes F.
    ssp. *allous* Geyer
    nicias Meigen
Cyaniris Dalman
  semiargus Rottemburg
Plebicula Higgins
  dorylas Schiffermüller
  amanda Schneider

Lysandra Hemming
  coridon Poda·
  bellargus Rottemburg
Polyommatus Kluk
  icarus Rottemburg

Hesperiidae
Pyrgus Hübner
  malvae L.
  alveus Hübner·
  armoricanus Oberthur
  centaureae Rambur
Erynnis Schrank
  tages L.
Heteropterus Dumeril
  morpheus Pallas
Carterocephalus Lederer
  palaemon Pallas
  silvicolus Meigen
Thymelicus Hübner
  acteon Rottemburg
  lineola Ochsenheimer
  sylvestris Poda
Hesperia F.
  comma L.
Ochlodes Scudder
  venatus Bremer & Grey

Index of scientific names

127

Index of English names